Microbiology & Biotechnology

The Biozone Writing Team:

Tracey Greenwood

Lyn Shepherd

Richard Allan

Daniel Butler

Published by:
Biozone International Ltd
109 Cambridge Road, Hamilton 2034, New Zealand

Printed by REPLIKA PRESS PVT LTD

Distribution Offices:

United Kingdom & Europe	**Biozone Learning Media (UK) Ltd**, Scotland
	Telephone: +44 (131) 557 5060
	Fax: +44 (131) 557 5030
	Email: sales@biozone.co.uk
	Website: www.biozone.co.uk
USA, Canada, South America, Africa	**Biozone International Ltd**, New Zealand
	Telephone: +64 (7) 856 8104
	Freefax: 1-800717-8751 (USA-Canada only)
	Fax: +64 (7) 856 9243
	Email: sales@biozone.co.nz
	Website: www.biozone.co.nz
Asia & Australia	**Biozone Learning Media Australia**, Australia
	Telephone: +61 (7) 5575 4615
	Fax: +61 (7) 5572 0161
	Email: sales@biozone.com.au
	Website: www.biozone.com.au

© 2006 **Biozone International Ltd**
First Edition 2006
ISBN: 1-877329-73-8

Front cover photographs:
Micrograph of irregularly shaped macroconidia of the fungal pathogen Microsporum distortum. Image courtesy of CDC ©2006

Gene information. Image ©2005 JupiterImages Corporation www.clipart.com

Biology Modular Workbook Series

The Biozone *Biology Modular Workbook Series* has been developed to meet the demands of customers with the requirement for a modular resource which can be used in a flexible way. Like Biozone's popular Student Resource and Activity Manuals, these workbooks provide a collection of visually interesting and accessible activities, which cater for students with a wide range of abilities and background. The workbooks are divided into a series of chapters, each comprising an introductory section with detailed learning objectives and useful resources, and a series of write-on activities ranging from paper practicals and data handling exercises, to questions requiring short essay style answers. Material for these workbooks has been drawn from Biozone's popular, widely used manuals, but the workbooks have been structured with even greater ease of use and flexibility in mind. During the development of this series, we have taken the opportunity to improve the design and content, while retaining the basic philosophy of a student-friendly resource which spans the gulf between textbook and study guide. With its unique, highly visual presentation, it is possible to engage and challenge students, increase their motivation and empower them to take control of their learning.

Microbiology & Biotechnology

This title in the *Biology Modular Workbook Series* provides students with a set of comprehensive guidelines and highly visual worksheets through which to explore aspects of traditional and modern biotechnology. *Microbiology & Biotechnology* covers what is an overwhelmingly extensive topic area, encompassing not only gene technologies and their applications, but fermentation technology, cloning and tissue culture, bioremediation, enzyme technology, and genome research. Microorganisms play a central role in many biotechnological processes, and a knowledge of microbial structure and diversity is necessary background to an understanding of the topic. This workbook comprises five chapters, each of which corresponds to a broad area of either microbiology or biotechnology. These areas are explained through a series of one and two page activities, each of which explores a specific concept (e.g. dilution plating or restriction enzymes). Model answers (on CD-ROM) accompany each order free of charge. *Microbiology & Biotechnology* is a student-centred resource. Students completing the activities, in concert with their other classroom and practical work, will consolidate existing knowledge and develop and practise skills that they will use throughout their course. This workbook may be used in the classroom or at home as a supplement to a standard textbook. Some activities are introductory in nature, while others may be used to consolidate and test concepts already covered by other means. Biozone has a commitment to produce a cost-effective, high quality resource, which acts as a student's companion throughout their biology study. Please do not photocopy from this workbook; we cannot afford to provide single copies of workbooks to schools and continue to develop, update, and improve the material they contain.

Acknowledgements and Photo Credits

Royalty free images, purchased by Biozone International Ltd, are used throughout this workbook and have been obtained from the following sources: Corel Corporation from various titles in their Professional Photos CD-ROM collection; IMSI (International Microcomputer Software Inc.) images from IMSI's MasterClips® and MasterPhotosTM Collection, 1895 Francisco Blvd. East, San Rafael, CA 94901-5506, USA; ©1996 Digital Stock, Medicine and Health Care collection; ©Hemera Technologies Inc., 1997-2001; © 2005 JupiterImages Corporation www.clipart.com; ©Click Art, ©T/Maker Company; ©1994., ©Digital Vision; Gazelle Technologies Inc.; PhotoDisc®, Inc. USA, www.photodisc.com. The authors would also like to thank those who have contributed to this edition: • Bioengineering AG Switzerland for their photograph of a bioreactor • Bio-Rad Laboratories, Inc. for allowing us to photograph the Helios gene gun **EliLily**: ©2002 EliLily and Co. for the photo of humalog • Pharmacia (Aust) Ltd for photos of the DNA gel sequencing • Stacey Farmer and Greg Baillie, Waikato DNA Sequencing Facility for their assistance with material on DNA sequencing and PCR • Rosie Bradshaw, Institute of Molecular Biosciences, Massey University, for assistance in the gene technology section • Roslin Institute for their photo of Dolly • Raewyn Poole, University of Waikato, for information provided on transformation of *Acacia* • Genesis Research and Development Corp. Auckland, for the photo used on the HGP activity • ©1999 University of Kansas, for the photo of the incubator for culture of cell lines • David Wells (AgResearch) for photos on cloning • Liam Nolan, Leo Sanchez, and Burkhard Budel for contributions to the activities on the genetics of Antarctic springtails • Kapiti Cheeses NZ, for information and photos of cheese production • Villa Maria Wines (NZ) for their photos of wine production • Totem Graphics, for their clipart collection of plants and animals • TechPool Studios, for their clipart collection of human anatomy: Copyright ©1994, TechPool Studios Corp. USA (some images were modified by R. Allan and T. Greenwood) • Corel Corporation, for clipart of plants and animals from the Corel MEGAGALLERY collection • 3D models created using Poser IV, Curious Labs. Photos kindly provided by individuals or corporations have been identified by way of coded credits as follows: **BOB**: Barry O'Brien (Uni. of Waikato), **BH**: Brendan Hicks (Uni. of Waikato), **CDC**: Centers for Disease Control and Prevention, Atlanta, USA, **CF**: Conan Fee (Uni. of Waikato), **EII**: Education Interactive Imaging, **HGSI**: Dena Borchardt at Human Genome Sciences Inc., **MPI**: Max Planck Institute for Developmental Biology, Germany, **RA**: Richard Allan, **RCN**: Ralph Cocklin, **TG**: Tracey Greenwood, **VMW**: Villa Maria Wines, **WMU**: Waikato Microscope Unit

Also in this series:

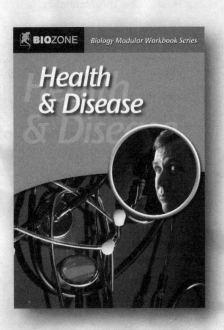

Health & Disease

ISBN: 1-877329-74-6

Skills in Biology

ISBN: 1-877329-71-1 (UK edition)

ISBN: 1-877329-72-X (International edition)

Contents

Activity is marked: ☐ to be done; ☑ when completed

How to Use this Workbook

Microbiology and Biotechnology is designed to provide students with a resource that will make the acquisition of knowledge and skills in these topics easier and more enjoyable. An understanding of the microbial world, and a working knowledge of the place of microorganisms in modern biotechnology are important in many biology curricula. This workbook is suitable for all students of biology, and will reinforce and extend the ideas developed by teachers. It is **not a textbook**; its aim is to complement the texts written for your particular course. *Microbiology and Biotechnology* provides the following resources in each chapter:

Guidance Provided for Each Topic

Learning objectives:

These provide you with a map of the chapter content. Completing the learning objectives relevant to your course will help you to satisfy the knowledge requirements of your syllabus. Your teacher may decide to leave out points or add to this list.

Chapter content:

The upper panel of the header identifies the general content of the chapter. The lower panel provides a brief summary of the chapter content.

Key words:

Key words are displayed in **bold** type in the learning objectives and should be used to create a glossary as you study each topic. From your teacher's descriptions and your own reading, write your own definition for each word.

Note: Only the terms relevant to your selected learning objectives should be used to create your glossary. Free glossary worksheets are also available from our web site.

Use the check boxes to mark objectives to be completed.
Use a **dot** to be done (•).
Use a **tick** when completed (✓).

Periodical articles:

Ideal for those seeking more depth or the latest research on a specific topic. Articles are sorted according to their suitability for student or teacher reference. Visit your school, public, or university library for these articles.

Internet addresses:

Access our database of links to more than **800** web sites (updated regularly) relevant to the topics covered. Go to Biozone's own web site: **www.thebiozone.com** and link directly to listed sites using the *BioLinks* button.

Supplementary texts:

References to supplementary texts suitable for use with this workbook are provided. Chapter references are provided as appropriate. The details of these are provided on page 8, together with other resources information.

Supplementary resources

Biozone's Presentation MEDIA are noted where appropriate.

Activity Pages

The activities and exercises make up most of the content of this workbook. They are designed to reinforce the concepts you have learned about in the topic. Your teacher may use the activity pages to introduce a topic for the first time, or you may use them to revise ideas already covered. They are excellent for use in the classroom, and as homework exercises and revision. In most cases, the activities should not be attempted until you have carried out the necessary background reading from your textbook. As a self-check, model answers for each activity are provided on CD-ROM with each order of workbooks.

Introductory paragraph:
The introductory paragraph sets the 'scene' for the focus of the page and provides important background information. Note any words appearing in **bold**; these are 'key words' which could be included in a glossary of biological terms for the topic.

Easy to understand diagrams:
The main ideas of the topic are represented and explained by clear, informative diagrams.

Tear-out pages:
Each page of the book has a perforation that allows easy removal. Your teacher may ask you to remove activity pages for marking, or so that they can be placed in a ringbinder with other work on the topic.

Write-on format:
You can test your understanding of the main ideas of the topic by answering the questions in the spaces provided. Where indicated, your answers should be concise. Questions requiring explanation or discussion are spaced accordingly. Answer the questions appropriately according to the specific questioning term used (see the facing page).

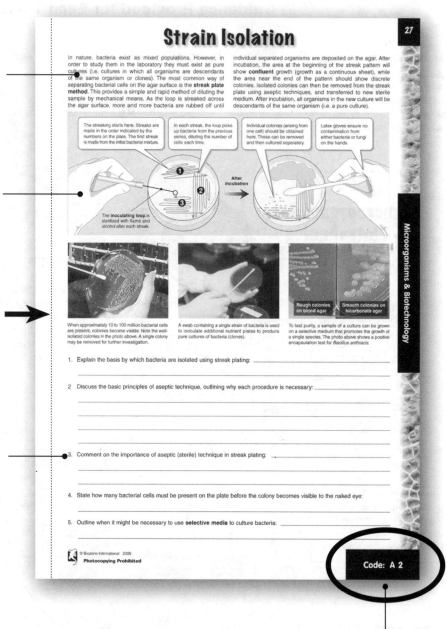

Activity Level
1 = Simple questions not requiring complex reasoning
2 = Some complex reasoning may be required
3 = More challenging, requiring integration of concepts

Type of Activity
D = Includes some data handling and/or interpretation
P = includes a paper practical
R = May require research outside the information on the page, depending on your knowledge base*
A = Includes application of knowledge to solve a problem
E = Extension material

* Material to assist with the activity may be found on other pages of the workbook or in textbooks.

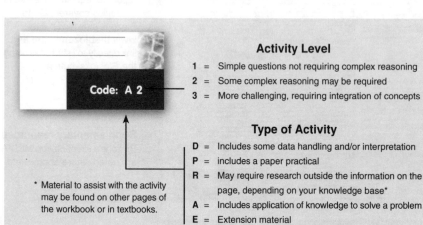

Code: A 2

Activity code:
Activities are coded to help you in identifying the type of activities and the skills they require. Most activities require some basic knowledge recall, but will usually build on this to include applying the knowledge to explain observations or predict outcomes. The least difficult questions generally occur early in the activity, with more challenging questions towards the end of the activity.

Explanation of Terms

Questions come in a variety of forms. Whether you are studying for an exam or writing an essay, it is important to understand exactly what the question is asking. A question has two parts to it: one part of the question will provide you with information, the second part of the question will provide you with instructions as to how to answer the question. Following these instructions is most important. Often students in examinations know the material but fail to follow instructions and do not answer the question appropriately. Examiners often use certain key words to introduce questions. Look out for them and be clear as to what they mean. Below is a description of terms commonly used when asking questions in biology.

Commonly used Terms in Biology

The following terms are frequently used when asking questions in examinations and assessments. Students should have a clear understanding of each of the following terms and use this understanding to answer questions appropriately.

Account for: Provide a satisfactory explanation or reason for an observation.

Analyse: Interpret data to reach stated conclusions.

Annotate: Add **brief** notes to a diagram, drawing or graph.

Apply: Use an idea, equation, principle, theory, or law in a new situation.

Appreciate: To understand the meaning or relevance of a particular situation.

Calculate: Find an answer using mathematical methods. Show the working unless instructed not to.

Compare: Give an account of similarities and differences between two or more items, referring to both (or all) of them throughout. Comparisons can be given using a table. Comparisons generally ask for similarities more than differences (see contrast).

Construct: Represent or develop in graphical form.

Contrast: Show differences. Set in opposition.

Deduce: Reach a conclusion from information given.

Define: Give the precise meaning of a word or phrase as concisely as possible.

Derive: Manipulate a mathematical equation to give a new equation or result.

Describe: Give a detailed account, including all the relevant information.

Design: Produce a plan, object, simulation or model.

Determine: Find the only possible answer.

Discuss: Give an account including, where possible, a range of arguments, assessments of the relative importance of various factors, or comparison of alternative hypotheses.

Distinguish: Give the difference(s) between two or more different items.

Draw: Represent by means of pencil lines. Add labels unless told not to do so.

Estimate: Find an approximate value for an unknown quantity, based on the information provided and application of scientific knowledge.

Evaluate: Assess the implications and limitations.

Explain: Give a clear account including causes, reasons, or mechanisms.

Identify: Find an answer from a number of possibilities.

Illustrate: Give concrete examples. Explain clearly by using comparisons or examples.

Interpret: Comment upon, give examples, describe relationships. Describe, then evaluate.

List: Give a sequence of names or other brief answers with no elaboration. Each one should be clearly distinguishable from the others.

Measure: Find a value for a quantity.

Outline: Give a brief account or summary. Include essential information only.

Predict: Give an expected result.

Solve: Obtain an answer using algebraic and/or numerical methods.

State: Give a specific name, value, or other answer. No supporting argument or calculation is necessary.

Suggest: Propose a hypothesis or other possible explanation.

Summarise: Give a brief, condensed account. Include conclusions and avoid unnecessary details.

In Conclusion

Students should familiarise themselves with this list of terms and, where necessary throughout the course, they should refer back to them when answering questions. The list of terms mentioned above is not exhaustive and students should compare this list with past examination papers / essays etc. and add any new terms (and their meaning) to the list above. The aim is to become familiar with interpreting the question and answering it appropriately.

Using the Internet

The internet is a vast global network of computers connected by a system that allows information to be passed through telephone connections. When people talk about the internet they usually mean the **World Wide Web** (WWW). The WWW is a service that has made the internet so simple to use that virtually anyone can find their way around, exchange messages, search libraries and perform all manner of tasks. The internet is a powerful resource for locating information. Listed below are two journal articles worth reading. They contain useful information on what the internet is, how to get started, examples of useful web sites, and how to search the internet.

- **Click Here: Biology on the Internet** Biol. Sci. Rev., 10(2) November 1997, pp. 26-29.
- **An A-level biologists guide to The World Wide Web** Biol. Sci. Rev., 10(4) March 1998, pp. 26-29.

Using the Biozone Website: www.thebiozone.com

The **Back** and **Forward** buttons allow you to navigate between pages displayed on a www site

The current **internet address (URL)** for the web site is displayed here. You can type in a new address directly into this space.

Tool bar provides a row of buttons with shortcuts for some commonly performed tasks, such as printing a page or 'refreshing' the page (i.e. making the page load again).

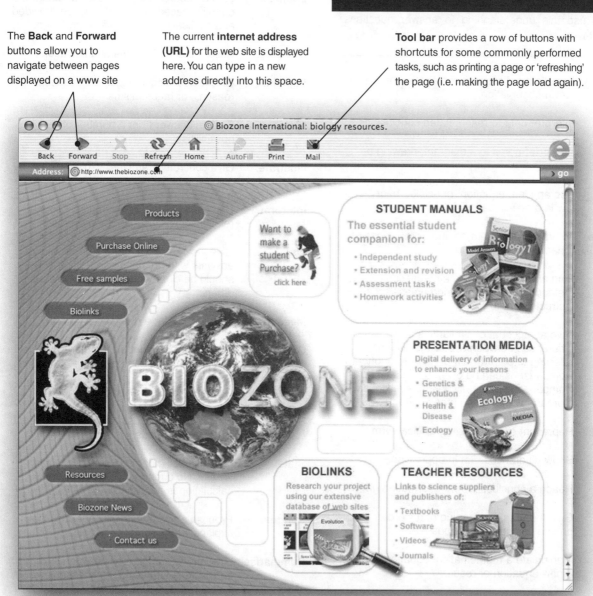

Searching the Net

The WWW addresses listed throughout the manual have been selected for their relevance to the topic in which they are listed. We believe they are good sites. Don't just rely on the sites that we have listed. Use the powerful 'search engines', which can scan the millions of sites for useful information. Here are some good ones to try:

Alta Vista:	**www.altavista.com**
Ask Jeeves:	**www.ask.com**
Excite:	**www.excite.com/search**
Google:	**www.google.com**
Go.com:	**www.go.com**
Lycos:	**www.lycos.com**
Metacrawler:	**www.metacrawler.com**
Yahoo:	**www.yahoo.com**

Biozone International provides a service on its web site that links to all internet sites listed in this workbook. Our web site also provides regular updates with new sites listed as they come to our notice and defunct sites deleted. Our BIO LINKS page, shown below, will take you to a database of regularly updated links to more than 800 other quality biology web sites.

The Resource Hub, accessed via the homepage or resources, provides links to the supporting resources referenced in the workbook. These resources include comprehensive and supplementary texts, biology dictionaries, computer software, videos, and science supplies. These can be used to enhance your learning experience.

Click on each topic to see a list of all related biology links. Each topic has relevant subtopics to make searching easier and each link has a brief description.

Index of sub-topics on this page. Click on these to jump down to the desired section.

Click on the link to access the named site. The brief description tells you how the site may be of interest, as well as any country specific bias, if this is relevant.

Concept Map for Microbiology and Biotechnology

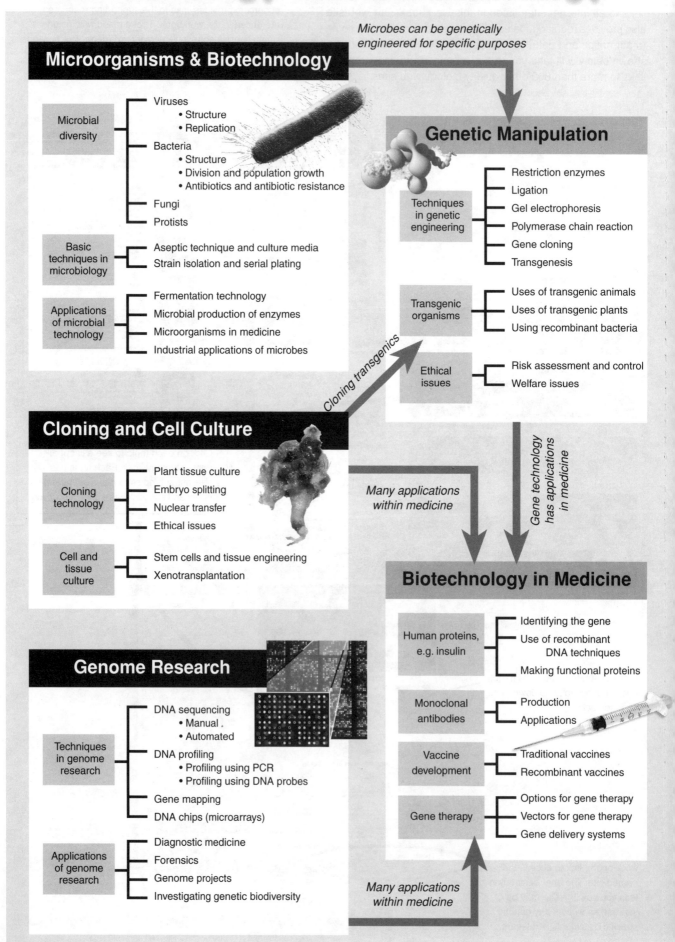

Microorganisms & Biotechnology

Microbial diversity
- Viruses
  - Structure
  - Replication
- Bacteria
  - Structure
  - Division and population growth
  - Antibiotics and antibiotic resistance
- Fungi
- Protists

Basic techniques in microbiology
- Aseptic technique and culture media
- Strain isolation and serial plating

Applications of microbial technology
- Fermentation technology
- Microbial production of enzymes
- Microorganisms in medicine
- Industrial applications of microbes

Microbes can be genetically engineered for specific purposes

Genetic Manipulation

Techniques in genetic engineering
- Restriction enzymes
- Ligation
- Gel electrophoresis
- Polymerase chain reaction
- Gene cloning
- Transgenesis

Transgenic organisms
- Uses of transgenic animals
- Uses of transgenic plants
- Using recombinant bacteria

Ethical issues
- Risk assessment and control
- Welfare issues

Cloning transgenics

Cloning and Cell Culture

Cloning technology
- Plant tissue culture
- Embryo splitting
- Nuclear transfer
- Ethical issues

Cell and tissue culture
- Stem cells and tissue engineering
- Xenotransplantation

Many applications within medicine

Gene technology has applications in medicine

Biotechnology in Medicine

Human proteins, e.g. insulin
- Identifying the gene
- Use of recombinant DNA techniques
- Making functional proteins

Monoclonal antibodies
- Production
- Applications

Vaccine development
- Traditional vaccines
- Recombinant vaccines

Gene therapy
- Options for gene therapy
- Vectors for gene therapy
- Gene delivery systems

Genome Research

Techniques in genome research
- DNA sequencing
  - Manual
  - Automated
- DNA profiling
  - Profiling using PCR
  - Profiling using DNA probes
- Gene mapping
- DNA chips (microarrays)

Applications of genome research
- Diagnostic medicine
- Forensics
- Genome projects
- Investigating genetic biodiversity

Many applications within medicine

Biotechnology is an area of applied science that has grown at an astonishing rate over the last three decades. Biotechnology has a profound effect on our use of other organisms, our impact on the environment, and our health. Some of the important areas of biotechnology covered in this workbook are mapped on the opposite page. A number of these technologies are relatively new, while others are well established but progressing rapidly (see *Some Landmarks in Modern Biotechnology*).

Some Landmarks in Modern Biotechnology

1973 First successful genetic engineering experiments are conducted when a gene from one bacterium is transferred into another and shown to work in the new host.

1977 Somatostatin is the first human protein to be produced by genetically engineered bacteria.

1978 First "test-tube baby" is born.

1981 The first GE plant is made and US courts decide that GE microbes can be patented.

1982 First approval is given for the environmental release of GE microorganisms.

　　　GE insulin becomes available to diabetics.

1987 The US Patent and Trademark Office announces that non-human animals are patentable.

1988 The US Patent and Trademark Office issues the first patent for a vertebrate, a GE mouse.

1989 Microorganisms are used to clean up the oil spill from the wrecked oil tanker Exon Valdez.

　　　First **microarray** developed by Stephen Fodor and his colleagues.

1990 The first genetically engineered food additive, an enzyme called rennin, is approved by the USFDA.

　　　First attempt at human gene therapy where doctors at the NIH transfuse a young girl with white blood cells genetically engineered to produce an essential immune protein that her own cells do not produce.

　　　Human Genome Project (HGP) formally launched with a $3 billion budget and 15 year completion date.

1991 First GE biocontrol agent goes on sale in the US.

1997 A GE rice, resistant to a widespread bacterial disease, is released for introduction to locally important rice varieties.

1998 First successful cloning of stem cells paves way for tissue rejuvenation by stem cell implantation and organ culture.

　　　Rival commercial project by Celera Genomics in Rockwell, Maryland, aims to finish human sequence in two years.

2000 First draft of human genome completed.

　　　First plant genome sequenced: thale cress, *Arabidopsis thaliana*.

2001 First successful transplant of an artificial heart.

2002 Rice and mosquito genomes sequenced.

2003 The second and third generation of biotech crops are expected on the market.

　　　HGP announce the more complete (99%) and higher quality human genome sequence.

　　　New Coronavirus is identified as the cause of SARS and its genome sequenced.

2004 HGP produces the finished sequence for euchromatin. Human gene number is revised down to only 20 000-25 000.

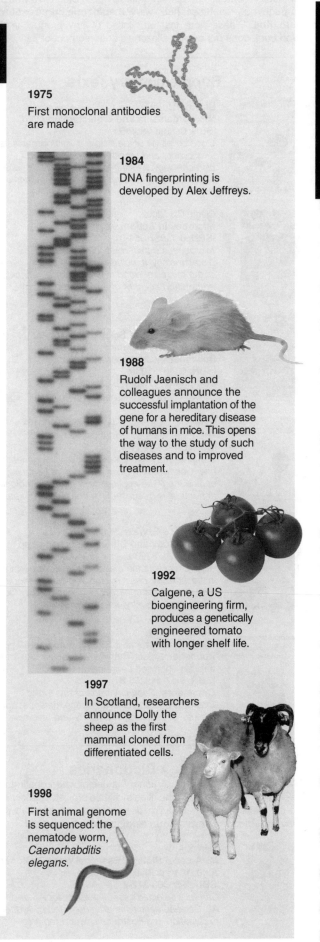

1975
First monoclonal antibodies are made

1984
DNA fingerprinting is developed by Alex Jeffreys.

1988
Rudolf Jaenisch and colleagues announce the successful implantation of the gene for a hereditary disease of humans in mice. This opens the way to the study of such diseases and to improved treatment.

1992
Calgene, a US bioengineering firm, produces a genetically engineered tomato with longer shelf life.

1997
In Scotland, researchers announce Dolly the sheep as the first mammal cloned from differentiated cells.

1998
First animal genome is sequenced: the nematode worm, *Caenorhabditis elegans.*

Resources Information

Your set textbook should always be a starting point for information, but there are also many other resources available. A list of readily available resources is provided below. Access to the publishers of these resources can be made directly from Biozone's web site through our resources hub: **www.thebiozone.com/resource-hub.html**. Please note that our listing of any product in this workbook does not denote Biozone's endorsement of it.

Supplementary Texts

Chenn, P., 1997.
Microorganisms and Biotechnology, 176 pp.
ISBN: 0-71957-509-5
Good coverage of the nature of microorganisms, their culture and growth, and their roles in biotechnology. It includes chapters on the genetic engineering of microbes and enzyme technology.

Clegg, C.J., 2002.
Microbes in Action, 92 pp.
ISBN: 0-71957-554-0
Microbes and their roles in disease and biotechnology. It includes material on the diversity of the microbial world, microbiological techniques, and a short account of enzyme technology.

Freeland, P., 1999
Hodder Advanced Science: Microbes, Medicine, and Commerce, 160 pp.
Publisher: Hodder and Stoughton
ISBN: 0340731036
Comments: *Coverage of biotechnology, microbiology, pathology, and immunity.*

Jones, N., A. Karp., & G. Giddings, 2001.
The Essentials of Genetics, 224 pp.
ISBN: 0-7195-8611-9
Comprehensive supplementary text for genetics and evolution, with good coverage of genetic engineering. The application of gene technologies to humans is discussed in a concluding chapter.

Lowrie, P. & S. Wells, 2000.
Microbiology and Biotechnology, 112 pp.
ISBN: 0521787238
This text covers the microbial groups important in biotechnology, basic microbiological techniques, and the various applications of microbes in food technology, industry, and medicine.

Taylor, J., 2001.
Microorganisms and Biotechnology, 192 pp.
Publisher: NelsonThornes. Available in Australia through Thomson Learning
ISBN: 0-17-448255-8
Comments: *Good coverage of this topic, including pathogens and disease, defence, and the use of microbes in industry and medicine.*

Biology Dictionaries

Access to a good biology dictionary is useful when dealing with biological terms. Some of the titles available are listed below. Link to the relevant publisher via Biozone's resources hub or by typing: **www.thebiozone.com/resources/dictionaries-pg1.html**

Clamp, A.
AS/A-Level Biology. Essential Word Dictionary, 2000, 161 pp. Philip Allan Updates.
ISBN: 0-86003-372-4.
Carefully selected essential words for AS and A2. Concise definitions are supported by further explanation and illustrations where required.

Hale, W.G., J.P. Margham, & V.A. Saunders
Collins: Dictionary of Biology 3 ed. 2003, 672 pp. HarperCollins. **ISBN**: 0-00-714709-0.
Updated to take in the latest developments in biology from the Human Genome Project to advancements in cloning (new edition pending).

Henderson, I.F, W.D. Henderson, and E. Lawrence.
Henderson's Dictionary of Biological Terms, 1999, 736 pp. Prentice Hall. **ISBN**: 0582414989
This edition has been updated, rewritten for clarity, and reorganised for ease of use. An essential reference and the dictionary of choice for many.

King, R.C. & W.D. Stansfield **A Dictionary of Genetics**, 6 ed., 2002, 544 pp. Oxford Uni. Press.
ISBN: 0-19-514325-6
A dictionary specifically addressing the needs of students and teachers for an up to date reference source for genetics and related fields.

McGraw-Hill (ed). **McGraw-Hill Dictionary of Bioscience**, 2 ed., 2002, 662 pp. McGraw-Hill.
ISBN: 0-07-141043-0
22 000 entries encompassing more than 20 areas of the life sciences. It includes synonyms, acronyms, abbreviations, and pronunciations for all terms.

Rudin, N.
Dictionary of Modern Biology (1997), 504 pp.
Barron's Educational Series Inc
ISBN: 0812095162.
More than 6000 terms in biosciences defined for college level students. Includes extensive cross referencing and several useful appendices.

Periodicals, Magazines, and Journals

Biological Sciences Review: *An informative quarterly publication for biology students.* Enquiries: Philip Allan Publishers, Market Place, Deddington, Oxfordshire OX 15 OSE **Tel**: 01869 338652 **Fax**: 01869 338803 **E-mail**: sales@philipallan.co.uk *or subscribe from their web site.*

New Scientist: *Widely available weekly magazine with research summaries and features.* Enquiries: Reed Business Information Ltd, 51 Wardour St. London WIV 4BN **Tel**: (UK and intl):+44 (0) 1444 475636 **E-mail**: ns.subs@qss-uk.com *or subscribe from their web site.*

Scientific American: *A monthly magazine containing specialist features. Articles range in level of reading difficulty and assumed knowledge.* Subscription enquiries: 415 Madison Ave. New York. NY10017-1111 **Tel**: (outside North America): 515-247-7631 **Tel**: (US& Canada): 800-333-1199

School Science Review: *A quarterly journal which includes articles, reviews, and news on current research and curriculum development. Free to Ordinary Members of the ASE or available on subscription.* Enquiries: **Tel**: 01707 28300 **Email**: info@ase.org.uk *or visit their web site.*

The American Biology Teacher: *The peer-reviewed journal of the NABT. Published nine times a year and containing information and activities relevant to biology teachers.* Contact: NABT, 12030 Sunrise Valley Drive, #110, Reston, VA 20191-3409 **Web**: www.nabt.org

Microorganisms & Biotechnology

Understanding the diversity of microorganisms and their role in modern biotechnology

Features of microbial groups (viruses, bacteria, fungi), techniques in microbial culture, microorganisms in industry and food production.

Learning Objectives

☐ 1. Compile your own glossary from the **KEY WORDS** displayed in **bold type** in the learning objectives below.

Introduction to Microorganisms *(pages 11-12)*

☐ 2. Understand what is meant by the term **microorganism**. Recognise the place of microbial groups within a **five kingdom classification system**. Appreciate that the **Archaebacteria** are increasingly being regarded as a separate (sixth) Kingdom.

☐ 3. Describe the **distinguishing features** of the following microorganisms: viruses, **Prokaryotae**, **Fungi**, and **Protista** (Protoctista). Describe the organisation of the genetic material inside bacterial cells and viral particles and understand how it differs from that of eukaryotes.

Viruses *(pages 13-16)*

☐ 4. Describe the structural features of viruses, including reference to the **capsid**, nucleic acid, envelope, and spikes. Identify the genetic and morphological features important in distinguishing different viral types.

☐ 5. Describe the life cycles of selected representative viral types, including reference to the process of viral replication in the host cell. Examples could iclude:
   (a) The lysogenic bacteriophage **lambda** (λ)
   (b) The retrovirus, **Human Immunodeficiency Virus**.
   (c) An enveloped virus such as the **influenza virus**.

Bacteria *(pages 17-24)*

☐ 6. Describe the structure of a bacterial cell and its inclusions, as illustrated by *E. coli*. Include reference to: cell wall, cell surface membrane, nuclear zone, 70S ribosomes, **flagella**, and **plasmids**.

☐ 7. Recognise the diversity of bacteria, and their ecological and economic importance. Identify examples of pathogenic and commercially important species.

☐ 8. Describe the use of the **gram stain** as a means of identifying two broad groups of bacteria on the basis of cell wall structure. Describe the basis of the stain and relate this to the cell wall structure in each group.

☐ 9. Describe **binary fission** in bacteria and recognise it as the main method of bacterial reproduction.

☐ 10. Recognise phases of growth in bacterial populations, including the **lag phase**, **log** (exponential) **phase**, and **stationary phase**. Explain why growth does not usually continue exponentially and identify exceptions to this.

☐ 11. Describe the role of **antibiotics** in medicine and identify problems with their use. Describe the ways in which antibiotics work to inhibit the growth of bacteria.

☐ 12. Explain in principle how **antibiotic resistance** in bacteria arises and discuss the various mechanisms by which this resistance is achieved.

Fungi (yeasts and moulds) *(page 25)*

☐ 13. Describe the general characteristics of **fungi**, as illustrated by representative **moulds** (e.g. *Pencillium*) and **yeasts** (e.g. *Saccharomyces*). Identify differences in structure between these two groups of fungi.

Microbial Culture *(pages 26-28, 33-34)*

☐ 14. Identify some of the safety issues associated with working with microorganisms. With respect to work with microorganisms, identify **safe working practices** and explain why they are necessary.

☐ 15. Describe the *in vitro* growth requirements of bacteria and fungi. Your descriptions should include reference to carbon and nitrogen sources, mineral requirements, temperature, pH, and oxygen supply.

☐ 16. Distinguish between the various **growth media** used in the culture of microorganisms and understand why different media are appropriate to different organisms.

☐ 17. Demonstrate an ability to use **aseptic technique** to:
   (a) Prepare and inoculate **nutrient broths** (**liquid media**) and **nutrient agar** plates (**solid media**).
   (b) Use **streak plating** for **strain isolation**.

☐ 18. Describe the generalised growth curves of fungi and bacteria in **culture**. Identify the **lag phase**, the phase of rapid (sometimes exponential) growth, the **stationary phase**, and the **death phase**. Suggest how bacterial and fungal cultures might be maintained in the rapid phase of growth.

☐ 19. Compare methods used to measure growth in bacterial populations: **turbidimetry**, **dilution plating** (serial dilution), and **haemocytometer** counts. Identify advantages and drawbacks with each method. Distinguish between **total cell count** and **viable cell count** and discuss how the latter might be assessed.

Large scale production

☐ 20. With reference to the production of antibiotics (penicillin) or mycoprotein, distinguish between **batch culture** and **continuous culture**, and compare the advantages and disadvantages of these two methods.

☐ 21. Describe the design of an industrial scale **fermenter** (**bioreactor**). Identify the features associated with providing optimum culture conditions and describe problems associated with large scale fermentations.

☐ 22. Through practical activities or simulations, identify the effects of varying conditions (e.g. pH, temperature) on the growth of microorganisms.

Microorganisms in Industry *(pages 29-32, 35-38)*

☐ 23. Using named examples, describe the use of microorganisms and substrates in the production of alternative energy sources: **biogas** (e.g. methane) and **gasohol** (a mix of petrol and fuel alcohol or ethanol derived from the fermentation of organic waste).

☐ 24. Using named examples, describe the use of microorganisms in the treatment of industrial and domestic waste (e.g. sewage).

Enzyme technology

☐ 25. Distinguish between **intracellular** and **extracellular** enzymes and outline the basic procedure for the production of enzymes from microorganisms (including growth in culture and **downstream processing**).

☐ 26. Explain the advantages of enzyme isolation and **immobilisation** in industrial processes. Describe the properties necessary in the enzymes used in industry (e.g. thermostability).

☐ 27. Describe some of the commercial applications of microbial enzymes, e.g. **pectinases** and **rennin** in the food industry and **proteases** in biological detergents and the tanning industry.

☐ 28. Describe the basic operation of enzyme-based **biosensors** and identify some of their uses in industry, bioremediation, and medicine.

Microbial Fermentation and Food Production
(pages 29-30, 39-47)

☐ 29. Outline the history of traditional biotechnology practices including the use of yeast in bread production, the production of alcoholic beverages, and the manufacture of cultured milk products.

☐ 30. Explain the role of biotechnology in the large scale production of fermented foods and beverages (e.g. cheese, yoghurt, bread, wine, or beer) and tenderised meat. In each case, outline the processes and stages involved, the microorganisms used, and any features of importance (e.g. microbial metabolism, genetic modifications).

☐ 31. With reference to specific examples (e.g. **mycoprotein, yeast extract**), explain how microorganisms themselves can be used as a food source.

☐ 32. Appreciate the social, economic, ethical, and environmental implications of biotechnology and gene manipulation (especially the manipulation of organisms used in food production).

Microorganisms and Medicine *(pages 77-78)*

☐ 33. Recognise the importance of genetically modified microorganisms in the large scale production of human proteins (e.g. **insulin, human growth hormone, factor VIII**). Explain the reasons for using microorganisms in these cases. Describe in detail the steps involved in the production of a human protein by microorganisms.

Supplementary Texts

See page 8 for details of these texts:

■ Chenn, P., 1997. **Microorganisms and Biotechnology** (John Murray), chpt. 1-4, 7, 9.

■ Clegg, C.J., 2002. **Microbes in Action** (John Murray), chpt. 1-4, 6-8.

■ Freeland, P., 1999. **Microbes, Medicine and Commerce** (Hodder & Stoughton), chpt. 1-2, 4-9.

■ Lowrie, P. & S. Wells, 2000. **Microbiology and Biotechnology** (CUP), chpt. 1-3 and 4 as required.

■ Taylor, J., 2001. **Microorganisms and Biotechnology** (NelsonThornes), chpt. 1-6.

Periodicals

See page 8 for details of publishers of periodicals:

■ **Are Viruses Alive?** Scientific American, Dec. 2004, pp. 77-81. *Although viruses challenge our concept of what "living" means, they are vital members of the web of life. This account covers the nature of viruses, including viral replication and an evaluation of the status of viruses in the world.*

■ **Bacteria** National Geographic, 184(2) August 1993, pp. 36-61. *Structure and diversity of bacteria: the most abundant and useful organisms on Earth.*

■ **Yeast** Biol. Sci. Rev., 9(3) January 1997, pp. 10-13. *An account of the basic features of a much studied and commonly exploited microorganism: baker's yeast, Saccharomyces.*

Microorganisms and biotechnology

■ **Living Factories** New Scientist, 3 February 1996, pp. 28-31. *Enzyme and DNA technology in industrial processes.*

■ **Microbial Proteins Working for Man** Biol. Sci. Rev., 11(4) March 1999, pp. 6-7. *The uses of microbial products in industry and the environment.*

■ **Enzymes from Fungi** Biol. Sci. Rev., 13 (3) Jan. 2001, pp. 19-21. *A discussion of the production and applications of fungal enzymes.*

■ **Enzyme Technology** Biol. Sci. Rev., 12 (5) May 2000, pp. 26-27. *The range and importance of industrial enzymes in modern biotechnology.*

■ **Genetically Engineered Bacteria** Biol. Sci. Rev., 10(1) Sept. 1997, pp. 2-6. *Genetic engineering of bacteria for use in industry and the use of plasmids as vectors for transformation.*

■ **Ethanol: Brazil's Green Fuel** Biol. Sci. Rev., 13(1) Sept. 2000, pp. 27-29. *The production, environmental benefits, and problems associated with ethanol and gasohol as fuel.*

■ **Growth Industry** New Scientist, 15 Nov. 1997 (Inside Science). *A special report on biotechnology. Covers fermentation technology, genetic engineering, cloning, and grafting.*

Microorganisms in food & medicine

■ **Lactic Acid Bacteria** Biol. Sci. Rev., 11(3) Jan. 1999, pp. 10-12. *Lactic acid bacteria: their metabolism and central role they play in the production of fermented foods.*

■ **The Science of Bubbly** Scientific American, January 2003, pp. 68-73. *The science behind champagne production.*

■ **The Microbiology of Cheese** Biol. Sci. Rev., 15(4) April 2003, pp. 37-41. *The microbiology behind cheese-making and an account of different types of cheeses and how they are made. Included is a discussion of pasteurisation, the microbial cultures, ripening, and microbial fermentation.*

■ **Food Biotechnology** Biol. Sci. Rev., 8(3) Jan. 1996, pp. 25-27. *The use of genetic manipulation of various microorganisms in the food industry.*

■ **GM Food Safety Special Report** Scientific American, April 2001. *Special issue examining aspects of the GM food debate (excellent).*

■ **Food / How Altered?** National Geographic, May 2002, pp. 32-50. *An excellent account of the issue of "biotech foods". What are they, how altered are they, and how safe are they?*

■ **Filamentous Fungi as Cellular Factories** Biol. Sci. Rev., 9(5) May 1997, pp. 7-9. *The uses of fungi in biotechnology especially in enzyme and antibiotic production.*

■ **Biosensors** Biol. Sci. Rev., 15(4) April 2003, pp. 32-36. *An account of the uses of biosensors and the principles behind their operation.*

■ **Growth Hormones** Biol. Sci. Rev., 8(2) Nov. 1995, pp. 15-17. *Growth hormones: their role in growth regulation and their production using fermentation technology.*

■ **Insulin from Yeast** Biol. Sci. Rev., 10(2) Nov. 1997, pp. 30-32. *Genetic engineering to produce human insulin for the treatment of diabetes.*

■ **From Starter to Finish** American Biology Teacher, 67(2) Feb. 2005, pp. 96-101. *An experiment through which students investigate the production of sourdough breads to illustrate the use of industrial microoorganisms.*

■ **Antibiotic Resistance** Biol. Sci. Rev. Nov. 1999 pp. 28-30. *Spontaneous and acquired bacterial resistance to antibiotics. Includes explanations of the mechanisms by which this occurs.*

■ **Behind Enemy Lines** Scientific American, May 2001, pp. 46-53. *Understanding the basis of antibiotic resistance is important in developing more effective drugs against disease. This excellent account includes a discussion of the scope of bacterial resistance and its biochemical basis.*

Internet

See pages 4-5 of the manuals for details of how to access **Bio Links** from: **www.thebiozone.com**. From Bio Links, access sites under the topics:

BIOTECHNOLOGY > Applications in Biotechnology > Food Biotechnology: • Food for our future • Genetically modified food • GM food information > **Industrial Biotechnology:** • About industrial enzymes • Biotechnology in industry • Chapter 19: Industrial microbiology (includes cheese, alcohol, bread and more, and covers non-food microbiology) • Cheese production and cheese products ... *and others*

MICROBIOLOGY > General microbiology: • Bacteriology homepage • British Mycological Society • Dairy microbiology • Fundamentals of microbiology 101 • Microbiology webbed out • The microbial world... *and others*

Presentation MEDIA to support this topic:

Genetics & Evolution CD-ROM:
• Set 9: Gene Technology

Microbial Groups

In order to distinguish organisms, it is desirable to classify and name them (a science known as **taxonomy**). An effective classification system requires features that are distinctive to a particular group of organisms. Revised classification systems, recognising three domains (rather than five kingdoms) are now recognised as better representations of the true diversity of life.

However, for the purposes of describing the g... we are most familiar, the five kingdom system... still appropriate. The three kingdoms commonly a... microbiology are described below by means of d... brief summaries.

Kingdom: PROKARYOTAE (Bacteria)

- Also known as monerans or prokaryotes.
- Two major bacterial lineages are recognised: the primitive **Archaebacteria** and the more advanced **Eubacteria**.
- All have a prokaryotic cell structure: they lack the nuclei and chromosomes of eukaryotic cells, and have smaller (70S) ribosomes.
- Have a tendency to spread genetic elements across species barriers by sexual conjugation, viral transduction and other processes.
- Can reproduce rapidly by binary fission in the absence of sex.

- Have evolved a wider variety of metabolism types than eukaryotes.
- Bacteria grow and divide or aggregate into filaments or colonies of various shapes.
- They are taxonomically identified by their appearance (form) and through biochemical differences.

Species diversity: 10 000 + Bacteria are rather difficult to classify to the species level because of their relatively rampant genetic exchange, and because their reproduction is usually asexual.

Eubacteria

- Also known as 'true bacteria', they probably evolved from the more ancient Archaebacteria.
- Distinguished from Archaebacteria by differences in cell wall composition, nucleotide structure, and ribosome shape.
- Very diverse group comprises most bacteria.
- The **gram stain** provides the basis for distinguishing two broad groups of bacteria. It relies on the presence of peptidoglycan (unique to bacteria) in the cell wall. The stain is easily washed from the thin peptidoglycan layer of gram negative walls but is retained by the thick peptidoglycan layer of gram positive cells, staining them a dark violet colour.

Gram-Positive Bacteria

The walls of gram positive bacteria consist of many layers of peptidoglycan forming a thick, single-layered structure that holds the gram stain.

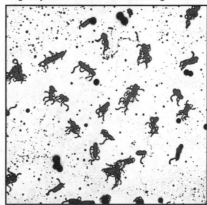

Bacillus alvei: a gram positive, flagellated bacterium. Note how the cells appear dark.

Gram-Negative Bacteria

The cell walls of gram negative bacteria contain only a small proportion of peptidoglycan, so the dark violet stain is not retained by the organisms.

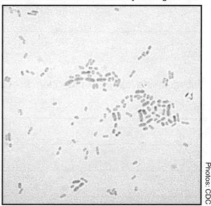

Photos: CDC

Alcaligenes odorans: a gram negative bacterium. Note how the cells appear pale.

Kingdom: FUNGI

- Heterotrophic.
- Rigid cell wall made of chitin.
- Vary from single celled to large multicellular organisms.
- Mostly saprotrophic (i.e. feeding on dead or decaying material).
- Terrestrial and immobile.

Examples:
Mushrooms/toadstools, yeasts, truffles, morels, moulds, and lichens.

Species diversity: 80 000 +

- **Lichens** are symbiotic associations of a fungus (provides protection) and an alga (provides the food).

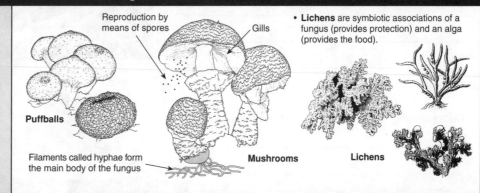

Reproduction by means of spores

Gills

Puffballs

Filaments called hyphae form the main body of the fungus

Mushrooms

Lichens

Kingdom: PROTISTA (PROTOCTISTA)

- A diverse group of organisms that do not fit easily into other taxonomic groups.
- Unicellular or simple multicellular.
- Widespread in moist or aquatic environments.

Examples of algae: green, brown, and red algae, dinoflagellates, diatoms.

Examples of protozoa: amoebas, foraminiferans, radiolarians, ciliates.

Species diversity: 55 000 +

Algae 'plant-like' protists

- Autotrophic (photosynthesis)
- Characterised by the type of chlorophyll present

Cell walls of cellulose, sometimes with silica

Diatom

Protozoa 'animal-like' protists

- Heterotrophic nutrition and feed via ingestion
- Most are microscopic (5 μm-250 μm)

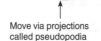

Lack cell walls

Move via projections called pseudopodia

Amoeba

CRAVEN COLLEGE

Features of Microbial Groups

A **microorganism** (or microbe) is literally a microscopic organism. The term is usually reserved for the organisms studied in microbiology: bacteria, fungi, microscopic protistans, and viruses. Most of these taxa also have macroscopic representatives. This is especially the case within the fungi. The distinction between a macrofungus and a microfungus is an artificial but convenient one. Unlike microfungi, which are made conspicuous by the diseases or decay they cause, macrofungi are the ones most likely to be observed with the naked eye. Examples of microfungi, which include yeasts and pathogenic species, are illustrated in this activity. These representatives of the fungal kingdom are those that most concern microbiologists.

1. Distinguishing features of Kingdom **Prokaryotae**:

_____
_____
_____
_____
_____
_____
_____
_____

2. Distinguishing features of Kingdom **Protista** (**Protoctista**):

_____
_____
_____
_____
_____
_____
_____
_____
_____

3. Distinguishing features of Kingdom **Fungi** (microfungi):

_____
_____
_____
_____
_____
_____
_____
_____
_____

Spirillum bacteria

Staphylococcus

Anabaena cyanobacterium

Foraminiferan

Spirogyra algae

Diatoms: *Pleurosigma*

Curvularia sp. conidiophore

Yeast cells in solution

Microsporum distortum (a pathogenic fungus)

The Structure of Viruses

Viruses are non-cellular **obligate intracellular parasites**, requiring a living host cell in order to reproduce. The traditional view of viruses is as a minimal particle, containing just enough genetic information to infect a host and highjack the host's machinery into replicating more viral particles. The identification in 2004 of a new family of viruses, called mimiviruses, is forcing a rethink of this conservative view. Mimiviruses overlap with parasitic cellular organisms in terms of both size (400 nm) and genome complexity (over 1000 genes) and their existence suggests a fourth domain of life. A typical, fully developed viral particle

(**virion**) lacks the metabolic machinery of cells, containing just a single type of nucleic acid (DNA or RNA) encased in a protein coat or **capsid**. Being non-cellular, they do not conform to the existing criteria upon which a five or six kingdom classification system is based. Viruses can be distinguished by their structure (see below) and by the nature of their genetic material (single or double stranded DNA or RNA). Those that use bacterial cells as a host (**bacteriophages**) can be grown on bacterial cultures, but other viruses are more difficult to study because they require living animals, embryos, or cell cultures in order to replicate.

Viral Structure

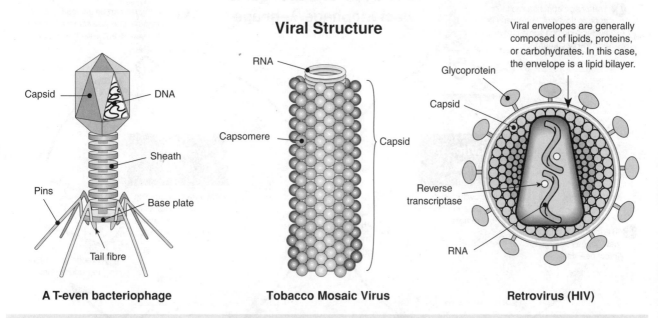

A T-even bacteriophage

Capsid — DNA — Sheath — Pins — Base plate — Tail fibre

Tobacco Mosaic Virus

RNA — Capsomere — Capsid

Retrovirus (HIV)

Viral envelopes are generally composed of lipids, proteins, or carbohydrates. In this case, the envelope is a lipid bilayer.

Glycoprotein — Capsid — Reverse transcriptase — RNA

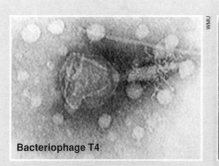

Bacteriophage T4:

Some viruses, particularly bacterial viruses (**bacteriophages**) are **complex viruses**, with complicated structures and capsids to which additional structures are attached.

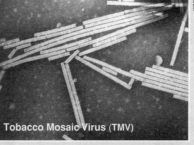

Tobacco Mosaic Virus (TMV)

TMV is a single stranded RNA plant virus, with a helical capsid. Helical viruses resemble long rods that may be rigid or flexible. The nucleic acid is found within a hollow, cylindrical capsid.

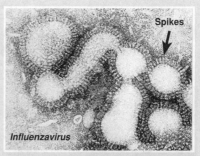

Influenzavirus

Spikes

In some viruses, the capsid is covered by an **envelope**, which protects the virus from the host's nuclease enzymes. *Influenzavirus* is an enveloped virus with many glycoprotein spikes.

1. Describe the basic structure of a generalised virus particle (virion): _____

_____

_____

2. Explain why viruses are such a difficult group to classify under conventional classification systems: _____

_____

_____

_____

_____

3. Describe the basis for viral identification: _____

_____

Microorganisms & Biotechnology

Replication in Bacteriophages

Viruses infect living cells, commanding the metabolism of the host cell and producing new viral particles. In some **bacteriophages**, this process may not immediately follow infection. Instead, the virus may enter a **lysogenic** or temperate cycle, integrating its nucleic acid into the host cell's to form a **prophage**. When in the lysogenic cycle, viral infection is said to be **latent** and the host cell is occupied by the virus and used to replicate the viral genes. The virus may become active again, entering the **lytic cycle** and utilising the host's cellular mechanisms to produce new virions. The lytic cycle results in death of the host cell through **lysis** of the cell. Bacteriophages can be grown in bacterial cultures on solid media where phage infection of bacterial cells will produce a clearing or **plaque**, visible against the lawn of bacterial growth. This forms the basis of a technique called **phage typing**, which is used in medicine for the diagnosis of bacterial strains when studying disease outbreaks (see below).

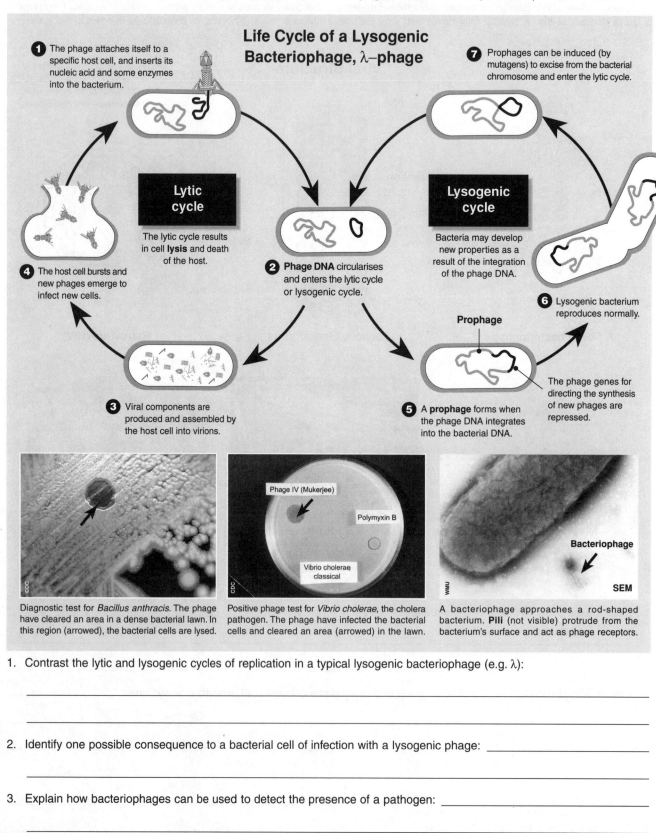

Life Cycle of a Lysogenic Bacteriophage, λ–phage

1 The phage attaches itself to a specific host cell, and inserts its nucleic acid and some enzymes into the bacterium.

7 Prophages can be induced (by mutagens) to excise from the bacterial chromosome and enter the lytic cycle.

Lytic cycle

The lytic cycle results in cell **lysis** and death of the host.

Lysogenic cycle

Bacteria may develop new properties as a result of the integration of the phage DNA.

4 The host cell bursts and new phages emerge to infect new cells.

2 **Phage DNA** circularises and enters the lytic cycle or lysogenic cycle.

6 Lysogenic bacterium reproduces normally.

Prophage

3 Viral components are produced and assembled by the host cell into virions.

5 A **prophage** forms when the phage DNA integrates into the bacterial DNA.

The phage genes for directing the synthesis of new phages are repressed.

Diagnostic test for *Bacillus anthracis*. The phage have cleared an area in a dense bacterial lawn. In this region (arrowed), the bacterial cells are lysed.

Phage IV (Mukerjee)
Polymyxin B
Vibrio cholerae classical

Positive phage test for *Vibrio cholerae*, the cholera pathogen. The phage have infected the bacterial cells and cleared an area (arrowed) in the lawn.

Bacteriophage
SEM

A bacteriophage approaches a rod-shaped bacterium. **Pili** (not visible) protrude from the bacterium's surface and act as phage receptors.

1. Contrast the lytic and lysogenic cycles of replication in a typical lysogenic bacteriophage (e.g. λ):

_____

_____

2. Identify one possible consequence to a bacterial cell of infection with a lysogenic phage: _____

_____

3. Explain how bacteriophages can be used to detect the presence of a pathogen: _____

_____

_____

Replication in Animal Viruses

There are some notable differences between replication in animal viruses and in bacteriophages. Animal viruses differ in their mechanisms for entering a host cell and, once the virus is inside, the way in which the new virions are produced and released is different. This is partly because of differences in host cell structure and metabolism and partly because the structure of animal viruses themselves is very variable. Enveloped viruses bud out from the host cell, whereas those without an envelope are released by rupture of the cell membrane. Three processes (attachment, penetration, and uncoating) are shared by both

DNA- and RNA containing animal viruses but the methods of biosynthesis vary between these two major groups. Generally, DNA viruses replicate their DNA in the nucleus of the host cell using viral enzymes, and synthesise their capsid and other proteins in the cytoplasm using the host cell's enzymes. This is outlined below for a typical enveloped DNA virus. RNA viruses are more variable in their methods of biosynthesis. The example overleaf describes replication in the retrovirus HIV, where the virus uses its own reverse transcriptase to synthesise viral DNA and produce **latent proviruses** or active, mature retroviruses.

Entry of an Enveloped Virus into a Cell

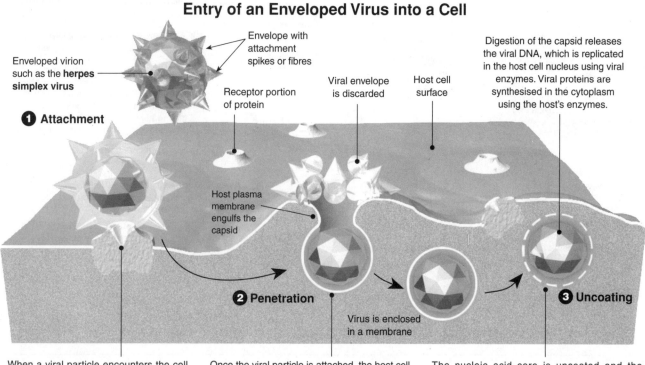

Enveloped virion such as the **herpes simplex virus**

Envelope with attachment spikes or fibres

Receptor portion of protein

Viral envelope is discarded

Host cell surface

Digestion of the capsid releases the viral DNA, which is replicated in the host cell nucleus using viral enzymes. Viral proteins are synthesised in the cytoplasm using the host's enzymes.

❶ **Attachment**

Host plasma membrane engulfs the capsid

❷ **Penetration**

Virus is enclosed in a membrane

❸ **Uncoating**

When a viral particle encounters the cell surface, it attaches to the **receptor sites** of proteins on the cell's plasma membrane.

Once the viral particle is attached, the host cell begins to engulf the virus by **endocytosis**. This is the cell's usual response to foreign particles.

The nucleic acid core is uncoated and the **biosynthesis** of new viruses begins. Mature virions are released by budding from the host cell.

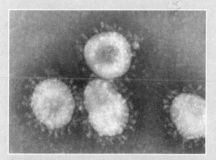

Coronaviruses are irregularly shaped viruses associated with upper respiratory infections and SARS. The envelope bears distinctive projections.

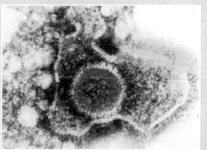

Herpesviruses are medium-sized enveloped viruses that cause various diseases including fever blisters, chickenpox, shingles, and herpes.

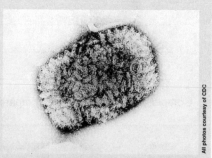

This *Vaccinia* virus belongs to the family of pox viruses; large (200-350 nm), enveloped DNA viruses that cause diseases such as smallpox.

All photos courtesy of CDC

Microorganisms & Biotechnology

1. Describe the purpose of the glycoprotein spikes found on some enveloped viruses: _____

_____

2. (a) Explain the significance of endocytosis to the entry of an enveloped virus into an animal cell: _____

_____

_____

   (b) State where an enveloped virus replicates its viral DNA: _____

   (c) State where an enveloped virus synthesises its proteins: _____

Code: A 2

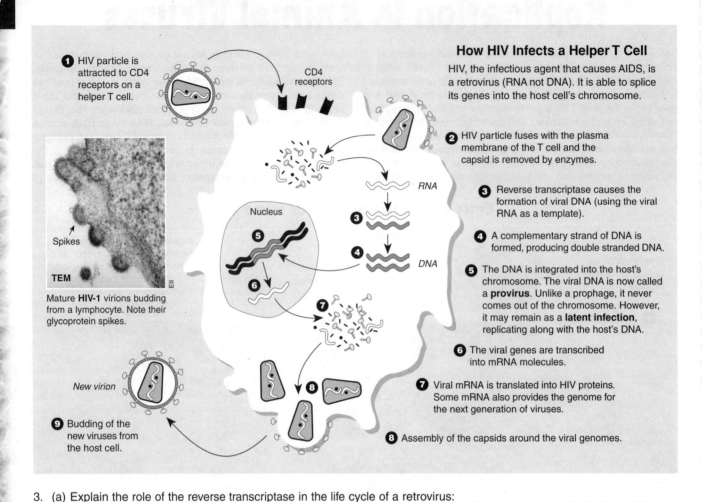

How HIV Infects a Helper T Cell

HIV, the infectious agent that causes AIDS, is a retrovirus (RNA not DNA). It is able to splice its genes into the host cell's chromosome.

1 HIV particle is attracted to CD4 receptors on a helper T cell.

CD4 receptors

2 HIV particle fuses with the plasma membrane of the T cell and the capsid is removed by enzymes.

RNA

3 Reverse transcriptase causes the formation of viral DNA (using the viral RNA as a template).

4 A complementary strand of DNA is formed, producing double stranded DNA.

DNA

Nucleus

5 The DNA is integrated into the host's chromosome. The viral DNA is now called a **provirus**. Unlike a prophage, it never comes out of the chromosome. However, it may remain as a **latent infection**, replicating along with the host's DNA.

6 The viral genes are transcribed into mRNA molecules.

7 Viral mRNA is translated into HIV proteins. Some mRNA also provides the genome for the next generation of viruses.

New virion

8 Assembly of the capsids around the viral genomes.

9 Budding of the new viruses from the host cell.

Spikes

TEM

Mature **HIV-1** virions budding from a lymphocyte. Note their glycoprotein spikes.

3. (a) Explain the role of the reverse transcriptase in the life cycle of a retrovirus: _____

_____

_____

(b) Explain the significance of the formation of a provirus: _____

_____

_____

_____

_____

4. Complete the following table comparing viral replication in bacteriophage and animal viruses:

Stage	Bacteriophage	Animal viruses
Attachment	Tail fibres attach to cell wall proteins	
Penetration	Viral DNA injected into host cell	
Uncoating	Not required	
Biosynthesis	In cytoplasm of host	In the nucleus and cytoplasm (DNA viruses) or cytoplasm (RNA viruses)
Chronic infection	Lysogeny (virus in lysogenic cycle)	
Release	Host cell is lysed	

Bacterial Cells

Bacterial (prokaryotic) cells are much smaller and simpler than the cells of eukaryotes. They lack many eukaryotic features (e.g. a distinct nucleus and membrane-bound cellular organelles). The bacterial cell wall is an important feature. It is a complex, multi-layered structure and often has a role in virulence. These pages illustrate some features of bacterial structure and diversity.

Structure of a Generalised Bacterial Cell

Plasmids: Small, circular DNA molecules (accessory chromosomes) which can reproduce independently of the main chromosome. They can move between cells, and even between species, by **conjugation**. This property accounts for the transmission of antibiotic resistance between bacteria. Plasmids are also used as vectors in recombinant DNA technology.

Single, circular main chromosome: Makes them haploid for most genes. It is possible for some genes to be found on both the plasmid and chromosome and there may be several copies of a gene on a group of plasmids.

The cell lacks a nuclear membrane, so there is no distinct nucleus and the chromosomes are in direct contact with the cytoplasm. It is possible for free ribosomes to attach to mRNA while the mRNA is still in the process of being transcribed from the DNA.

1 µm

Fimbriae: Hairlike structures that are shorter, straighter, and thinner than flagella. They are used for attachment, not movement. Pili are similar to fimbriae, but are longer and less numerous. They are involved in bacterial conjugation (below) and as phage receptors (opposite).

Cell surface membrane: Similar in composition to eukaryotic membranes, although less rigid.

Cytoplasm

Glycocalyx. A viscous, gelatinous layer outside the cell wall. It is composed of polysaccharide and/or polypeptide. If it is firmly attached to the wall, it is called a **capsule**. If loosely attached, it is called a **slime layer**. Capsules may contribute to virulence in pathogenic species, e.g. by protecting the bacteria from the host's immune attack. In some species, the glycocalyx allows attachment to substrates.

Cell wall. A complex, semi-rigid structure that gives the cell shape, prevents rupture, and serves as an anchorage point for flagella. The cell wall is composed of a macromolecule called **peptidoglycan**; repeating disaccharides attached by polypeptides to form a lattice. The wall also contains varying amounts of lipopolysaccharides and lipoproteins. The amount of peptidoglycan present in the wall forms the basis of the diagnostic **gram stain**. In many species, the cell wall contributes to their virulence (disease-causing ability).

Flagellum (pl. flagella). Some bacteria have long, filamentous appendages, called flagella, that are used for locomotion. There may be a single polar flagellum (monotrichous), one or more flagella at each end of the cell, or the flagella may be distributed over the entire cell (peritrichous).

Bacterial cell shapes

Most bacterial cells range between 0.20-2.0 µm in diameter and 2-10 µm length. Although they are a very diverse group, much of this diversity is in their metabolism. In terms of gross morphology, there are only a few basic shapes found (illustrated below). The way in which members of each group aggregate after division is often characteristic and is helpful in identifying certain species.

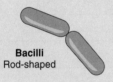

Bacilli
Rod-shaped

Bacilli: Rod-shaped bacteria that divide only across their short axis. Most occur as single rods, although pairs and chains are also found. The term bacillus can refer (as here) to shape. It may also denote a genus.

Cocci
Ball-shaped

Cocci: usually round, but sometimes oval or elongated. When they divide, the cells stay attached to each other and remain in aggregates e.g. pairs (diplococci) or clusters (staphylococci), that are usually a feature of the genus.

Spirilla
Spiral-shaped

Spirilla and vibrio: Bacteria with one or more twists. Spirilla bacteria have a helical (corkscrew) shape which may be rigid or flexible (as in spirochetes). Bacteria that look like curved rods (comma shaped) are called vibrios.

Bacterial conjugation

The two bacteria below are involved in conjugation: a one-way exchange of genetic information from a donor cell to a recipient cell. The plasmid, which must be of the 'conjugative' type, passes through a tube called a **sex pilus** to the other cell. Which is donor and which is recipient appears to be genetically determined. Conjugation should not be confused with sexual reproduction, as it does not involve the fusion of gametes or formation of a zygote.

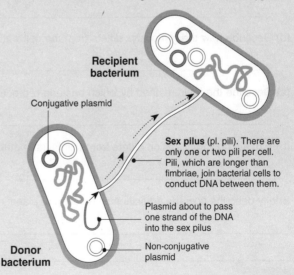

Recipient bacterium

Conjugative plasmid

Sex pilus (pl. pili). There are only one or two pili per cell. Pili, which are longer than fimbriae, join bacterial cells to conduct DNA between them.

Plasmid about to pass one strand of the DNA into the sex pilus

Non-conjugative plasmid

Donor bacterium

Microorganisms & Biotechnology

Code: RA 2

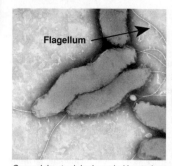

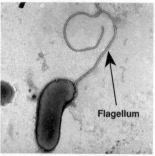

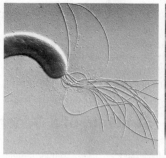

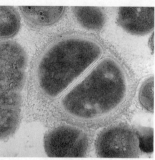

Campylobacter jejuni, a spiral bacterium responsible for foodborne intestinal disease. Note the single flagellum at each end (amphitrichous arrangement).

Helicobacter pylori, a comma-shaped vibrio bacterium that causes stomach ulcers in humans. This bacterium moves by means of multiple polar flagella.

A species of *Spirillum*, a spiral shaped bacterium with a tuft of polar flagella. Most of the species in this genus are harmless aquatic organisms.

Bacteria usually divide by binary fission. During this process, DNA is copied and the cell splits into two cells, as in these gram positive cocci.

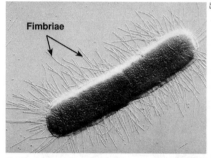

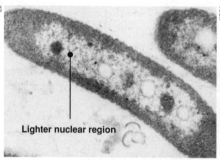

Escherichia coli, a common gut bacterium with **peritrichous** (around the entire cell) **fimbriae**. *E. coli* is a gram negative rod; it does not take up the gram stain but can be counter stained with safranin.

TEM showing *Enterobacter* bacteria, which belong to the family of gut bacteria commonly known as enterics. They are widely distributed in water, sewage, and soil. The family includes motile and non-motile species.

SEM of endospores of ***Bacillus anthracis*** bacteria, which cause the disease anthrax. These heat-resistant spores remain viable for many years and enable the bacteria to survive in a dormant state.

1. Describe three features distinguishing prokaryotic cells from eukaryotic cells:

   (a) _____

   (b) _____

   (c) _____

2. (a) Describe the function of flagella in bacteria: _____

   _____

   (b) Explain how fimbriae differ structurally and functionally from flagella: _____

   _____

   _____

3. (a) Describe the location and general composition of the bacterial cell wall: _____

   _____

   _____

   (b) Describe how the glycocalyx differs from the cell wall: _____

   _____

4. (a) Describe the main method by which bacteria reproduce: _____

   _____

   (b) Explain how conjugation differs from this usual method: _____

   _____

5. Briefly describe how the artificial manipulation of plasmids has been used for technological applications:

   _____

   _____

   _____

Growth in a Bacterial Population

Bacteria normally reproduce by a process called **binary fission**; a simple mitotic cell division that is preceded by cell elongation and involves one cell dividing in two. The time required for a cell to divide is the **generation time** and it varies between organisms and with environmental conditions such as temperature. When a few bacteria are inoculated into a liquid growth medium, and the population is counted at intervals, it is possible to plot a

bacterial growth curve that shows the growth of cells over time. In this activity, you will simulate this for a hypothetical bacterial population with a generation time of 20 minutes. In a bacterial culture with a limited nutrient supply, four growth phases are evident: the early **lag phase**, the **log phase** of exponential growth, the **stationary phase** when growth rate slows, and the **death** phase, when the population goes into logarithmic decline.

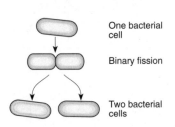

One bacterial cell

Binary fission

Two bacterial cells

Time (mins)	Population size
0	1
20	2
40	4
60	8
80	
100	
120	
140	
160	
180	
200	
220	
240	
260	
280	
300	
320	
340	
360	

1. Complete the table (above) by doubling the number of bacteria for every 20 minute interval.

2. Graph the results on the grid above. Make sure that you choose suitable scales for each axis. Label the axes and mark out (number) the scale for each axis. Identify the lag and log phases of growth and mark them on the graph.

3. State how many bacteria were present after: 1 hour: _____ 3 hours: _____ 6 hours: _____

4. Describe the shape of the curve you have plotted: _____

5. Predict what would happen to the shape of the growth curve of this population assuming no further input of nutrients:

_____

_____

Review of Bacterial Structure

Bacteria are prokaryotes: simple, unicellular organisms lacking a distinct nucleus or membrane-bound organelles. They are a very successful group, found in a wide range of habitats. In fact, the Earth's oldest fossils are bacteria dated at 3.5 billion years (in contrast to the oldest eukaryotic fossils at 800 million years old). Bacteria are important as pathogens and have a central role in the cycling of elements. Without them, the supply of biologically available nutrients would diminish and eventually disappear. Bacteria reproduce asexually and are therefore difficult to classify by conventional means. In some cases, pure cultures of the same species may not be identical. Such differing groups are called **strains**. Strains are cell lines derived from a single cell and identified by a specific number, letter, or name. It is within such strains that specific features such as antibiotic resistance arise.

Structure of a Generalised Bacterial Cell

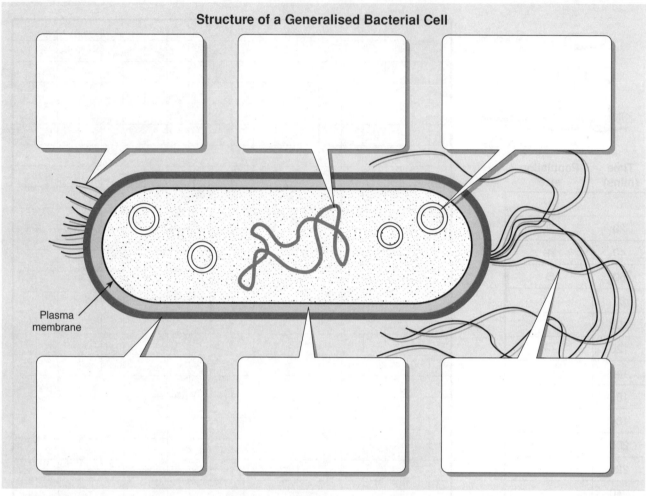

Plasma membrane

1. Complete the diagram above by labelling the boxes with organelles or structures they represent and briefly describe the function of each. Use the pages covering features of bacteria for help.

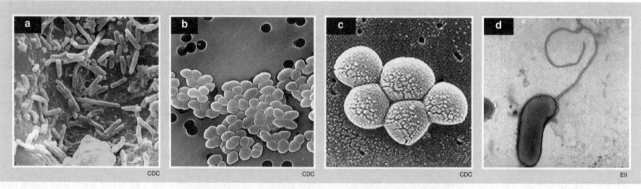

2. Using the correct terminology, identify the bacterial shapes shown in the photos above:

   (a) _____   (c) _____

   (b) _____   (d) _____

3. Identify the process by which bacteria generally reproduce: _____

4. Identify a species of economically important bacteria and state why it is important: _____
   _____

Code: RA 2

Antimicrobial Drugs

Antimicrobial drugs include synthetic (manufactured) **drugs** as well as drugs produced by bacteria and fungi, called **antibiotics**. Antibiotics are produced naturally by these microorganisms as a means of inhibiting competing microbes around them (a form of antibiosis, hence the name antibiotic). The first antibiotic, called penicillin, was discovered in 1928 by Alexander Fleming. Since then, similar inhibitory reactions between colonies growing on solid media have been commonly observed. Antibiotics are actually rather easy to discover, but few of them are of medical or commercial value. Many antibiotics are toxic to humans or lack any advantage over those already in use. More than half of our antibiotics are produced by species of filamentous bacteria that commonly inhabit the soil, called *Streptomyces*. A few antibiotics are produced by bacteria of the genus *Bacillus*. Others are produced by moulds, mostly of the genera *Cephalosporium* and *Penicillium*. Antimicrobial drugs are used in **chemotherapy** programmes to treat infectious diseases. Like disinfectants, these chemicals interfere with the growth of microorganisms (see diagram below). They may either kill microbes directly (**bactericidal**) or prevent them from growing (**bacteriostatic**). To be effective, they must often act inside the host, so their effect on the host's cells and tissues is important. The ideal antimicrobial drug has **selective toxicity**, killing the pathogen without damaging the host. Some antimicrobial drugs have a narrow **spectrum of activity**, and affect only a limited number of microbial types. Others are **broad-spectrum drugs** and affect a large number of microbial species (see the table below). When the identity of a pathogen is not known, a broad-spectrum drug may be prescribed in order to save valuable time. There is a disadvantage with this, because broad spectrum drugs target not just the pathogen, but much of the host's normal microflora also. The normal microbial community usually controls the growth of pathogens and other microbes by competing with them. By selectively removing them with drugs, certain microbes in the community that do not normally cause problems, may flourish and become **opportunistic pathogens**.

How Antimicrobial Drugs Work

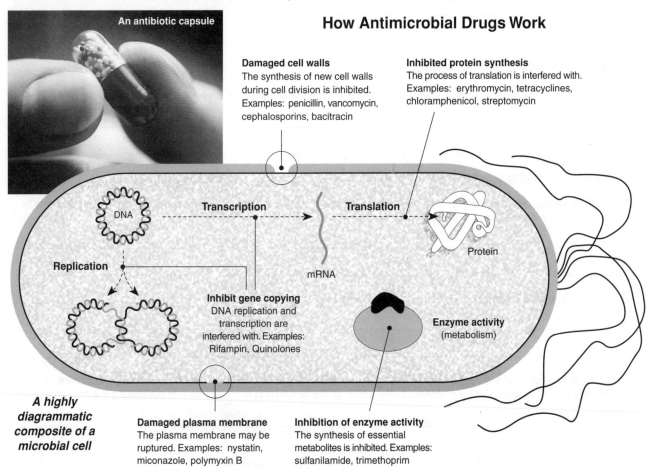

An antibiotic capsule

Damaged cell walls
The synthesis of new cell walls during cell division is inhibited. Examples: penicillin, vancomycin, cephalosporins, bacitracin

Inhibited protein synthesis
The process of translation is interfered with. Examples: erythromycin, tetracyclines, chloramphenicol, streptomycin

Transcription

Translation

DNA

mRNA

Protein

Replication

Inhibit gene copying
DNA replication and transcription are interfered with. Examples: Rifampin, Quinolones

Enzyme activity
(metabolism)

A highly diagrammatic composite of a microbial cell

Damaged plasma membrane
The plasma membrane may be ruptured. Examples: nystatin, miconazole, polymyxin B

Inhibition of enzyme activity
The synthesis of essential metabolites is inhibited. Examples: sulfanilamide, trimethoprim

Spectrum of antimicrobial activity of a number of chemotherapeutic drugs

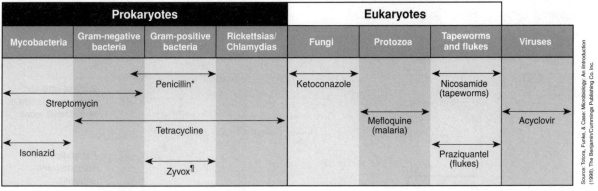

Prokaryotes				Eukaryotes			
Mycobacteria	Gram-negative bacteria	Gram-positive bacteria	Rickettsias/ Chlamydias	Fungi	Protozoa	Tapeworms and flukes	Viruses
		Penicillin*		Ketoconazole		Nicosamide (tapeworms)	
Streptomycin							
		Tetracycline			Mefloquine (malaria)		Acyclovir
Isoniazid						Praziquantel (flukes)	
		Zyvox¶					

Source: Totora, Funke, & Case: Microbiology: An Introduction (1998), The Benjamin/Cummings Publishing Co. Inc.

* There are some synthetic derivatives of penicillin that act effectively against gram-negative bacteria.
¶ The first new class of antibiotics to be used in 35 years.

Microorganisms & Biotechnology

Code: A 2

1. Discuss the requirements of an "ideal" antimicrobial drug, and explain in what way antibiotics satisfy these requirements:

_____

_____

_____

_____

2. Some bacteria have ways of tolerating treatment by antibiotics, and are termed 'superbugs'.

   (a) Explain what is meant by **antibiotic resistance** in bacteria: _____

   _____

   _____

   (b) Explain why a course of antibiotics should be finished completely, even when the symptoms of infection have gone:

   _____

   _____

3. The spectrum of activity varies for different groups of drugs.

   (a) Explain the advantages and disadvantages of using a broad-spectrum drug on an unidentified bacterial infection:

   _____

   _____

   (b) Identify two broad spectrum groups of drugs: _____

4. Although there are a few drugs that have some success in controlling viruses, antibiotics are ineffective. Explain why antibiotics do not work against viruses:

   _____

   _____

5. Describe four ways in which antimicrobial drugs kill or inhibit the growth of microbes: _____

   _____

   _____

6. The diagram below shows an experiment investigating the effectiveness of different antibiotics on a pure culture of a single species of bacteria. Giving a reason, state which antibiotic (A-D) is most effective in controlling the bacteria:

   _____

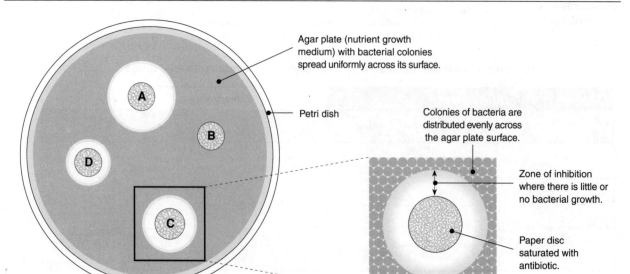

Agar plate (nutrient growth medium) with bacterial colonies spread uniformly across its surface.

Petri dish

Colonies of bacteria are distributed evenly across the agar plate surface.

Zone of inhibition where there is little or no bacterial growth.

Paper disc saturated with antibiotic.

Antibiotic Resistance

Antibiotics are drugs that fight bacterial infections. After being discovered in the 1940s, they rapidly transformed medical care and dramatically reduced illness and death from bacterial disease. However, with increased and often indiscriminate antibiotic use, many bacteria quickly developed drug resistance. The increasing number of **multi-drug resistant** strains is particularly worrying; resistant infections inhibit the treatment of patients and increase mortality. Antibiotic resistance also adds considerably to the costs of treating disease and, as resistance spreads, new drugs have an increasingly limited life span during which they are effective. Resistant bacteria include *Klebsiella*, *Enterococcus*, *E. coli*, *Staphylococcus aureus*, *Enterobacter*, *Pseudomonas*, and *Mycobacterium tuberculosis* and their resistance has developed through three main mechanisms (below right).

Methods by which Bacteria Acquire Resistance

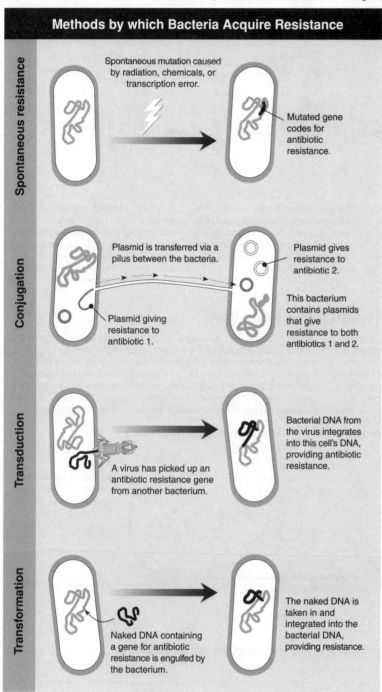

Spontaneous resistance

Spontaneous mutation caused by radiation, chemicals, or transcription error.

Mutated gene codes for antibiotic resistance.

Conjugation

Plasmid is transferred via a pilus between the bacteria.

Plasmid gives resistance to antibiotic 2.

This bacterium contains plasmids that give resistance to both antibiotics 1 and 2.

Plasmid giving resistance to antibiotic 1.

Transduction

A virus has picked up an antibiotic resistance gene from another bacterium.

Bacterial DNA from the virus integrates into this cell's DNA, providing antibiotic resistance.

Transformation

Naked DNA containing a gene for antibiotic resistance is engulfed by the bacterium.

The naked DNA is taken in and integrated into the bacterial DNA, providing resistance.

Mechanisms of Resistance

Inactivation

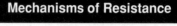
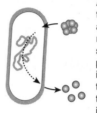

A mutated enzyme produced in the bacterium destroys the antibiotic. Many bacteria that are resistant to penicillin possess such an enzyme (called penicillinase). Penicillinase inactivates penicillin by catalysing the destruction of bonds within the penicillin molecule, thereby inactivating it.

Alteration of target

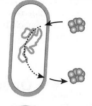

Some antibiotics (e.g. streptomycin) inhibit bacterial protein synthesis. However, if only one amino acid in either of two positions on a ribosome is replaced, a bacterium can develop streptomycin resistance.

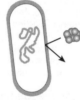

Some antibiotics, such as penicillin, interfere with cell wall synthesis. Therefore mutations to the cell wall proteins can result in resistance.

Alteration of permeability

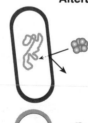

In order to be effective, antibiotics have to get into the bacterial cell and interfere with its cellular processes. Bacterial cells can acquire resistance by excluding the antibiotic or by slowing down its entry enough to render the antibiotic ineffective.

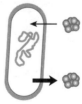

Bacteria can develop proteins that actively pump antibiotics out of their cell faster than the antibiotics can enter.

Microorganisms & Biotechnology

1. Explain how spontaneous resistance can occur in a bacterium:

_____

_____

2. Explain how the misuse of antibiotics by patients can lead to the development of antibiotic resistant bacteria:

_____

_____

_____

Evolution in Bacteria

As a result of their short **generation times**, bacterial populations can show significant evolutionary change within relatively short periods of time. The development of **antibiotic resistance** is one such evolutionary change and it arises and spreads within and between bacterial populations with frightening ease. A variety of human practices have led to antibiotic resistance and have increased the rate at which bacterial strains acquire new properties.

These practices include the overuse and misuse of antibiotics by physicians, the use of antibiotics by immunosuppressed patients to prevent infection, the use of antibiotics in animal feed, and the spread of resistant bacteria to new areas because of air travel. For many strains of pathogenic bacteria, resistant mutants are increasingly replacing susceptible normal populations. This makes the search for new types of antibiotics increasingly urgent.

The Evolution of Drug Resistance in Bacteria

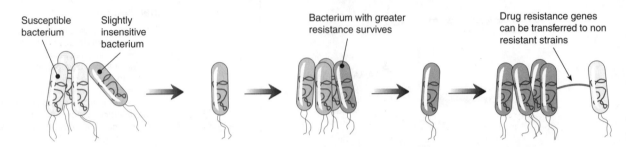

Susceptible bacterium | Slightly insensitive bacterium | Bacterium with greater resistance survives | Drug resistance genes can be transferred to non resistant strains

Within any population, there is genetic variation. In this case, the susceptibility of the bacterial strain is normally distributed, with some cells being more susceptible than others.

If the amount of antibiotic delivered is too low, or the full course of antibiotics is not completed, only the most susceptible bacteria will die.

Now a population of insensitive bacteria has developed. Within this population there will also be variation in the susceptibility to antibiotics. As treatment continues, some of the bacteria may acquire greater resistance.

A highly resistant population has evolved. The resistant cells can exchange genetic material with other bacteria, passing on the resistance genes. The antibiotic that was initially used against this bacterial strain will now be ineffective against it.

Observing Adaptive Radiation

Recently, scientists have demonstrated rapid evolution in bacteria. *Pseudomonas fluorescens* was used in the experiment and propagated in a simple heterogeneous environment consisting of a 25 cm³ glass container containing 6 cm³ of broth medium. Over a short period of time, the bacteria underwent morphological diversification, with a number of new morphs appearing. These morphs were shown to be genetically distinct. A striking feature of the evolved species is their niche specificity, with each new morph occupying a distinct habitat (below, left). In a follow up experiment (below, right), the researchers grew the same original bacterial strain in the same broth under identical incubation conditions, but in a homogeneous environment (achieved by shaking the broth). Without the different habitats offered by an undisturbed environment, no morphs emerged. The experiment illustrated the capacity of bacteria to evolve to utilise available niches.

Heterogeneous environment

WS bacteria (wrinkly morphology) evolved to colonise the air-broth interface.

The FS species (fuzzy morphology) colonised the bottom of the container.

Homogeneous environment

Because there is only one niche, no adaptive radiation occurs.

The ancestral SM species (smooth morphology) colonised the surface of the broth.

1. Using an illustrative example, explain why evolution of new properties in bacteria can be very rapid: _____

_____

_____

2. (a) In the example above, suggest why the bacteria evolved when grown in a heterogeneous environment:

_____

_____

(b) Predict what would happen if the FS morph was cultured in the homogeneous environment:

_____

_____

Fungi

The fungi are a large, successful group of eukaryotes that includes the yeasts, moulds, and fleshy fungi. The study of fungi is called **mycology**. All fungi are chemoheterotrophs: they lack chlorophyll and require organic compounds for a source of energy and carbon. Most fungi are also **saprophytic**, feeding on dead material, although some are parasitic or mutualistic. Fungal nutrition is absorptive and digestion is extracellular and takes place outside the fungal body. Of more than 100 000 fungal species, only about 100 are pathogenic to humans or other animals. However, many are plant pathogens and virtually every economically important plant species is attacked by one or more fungi. Note that the **lichens** have been reclassified into the fungal kingdom. They are dual organisms, formed by a mutualistic association between a green alga or a cyanobacterium, and a fungus (usually an ascomycete). Features of two fungal groups: yeasts and moulds are described below.

Single Celled Fungi: Yeasts

Yeasts are nonfilamentous, unicellular fungi that are typically spherical or oval shaped. Yeasts reproduce asexually by fission or budding. They are facultative anaerobes, a property that is exploited in the brewing, wine making, and bread making industries.

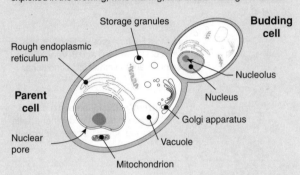

Filamentous Fungi: Moulds

Moulds are multicellular, filamentous fungi often divided by septa into uni-nucleate, cell-like units. When conditions are favourable, hyphae grow to form a filamentous mass called a **mycelium.**

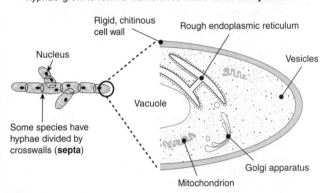

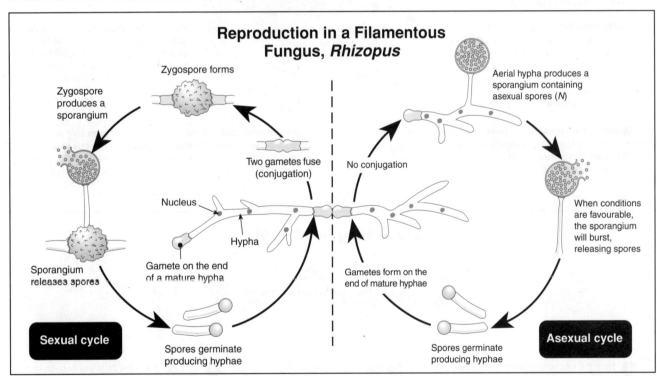

Reproduction in a Filamentous Fungus, *Rhizopus*

Sexual cycle

Zygospore forms

Zygospore produces a sporangium

Sporangium releases spores

Spores germinate producing hyphae

Gamete on the end of a mature hypha

Nucleus

Hypha

Two gametes fuse (conjugation)

No conjugation

Asexual cycle

Aerial hypha produces a sporangium containing asexual spores (N)

When conditions are favourable, the sporangium will burst, releasing spores

Gametes form on the end of mature hyphae

Spores germinate producing hyphae

1. List three distinguishing features of fungi: _____

   _____

2. Outline the key differences in the reproductive strategies of yeasts and moulds: _____

   _____

   _____

3. Identify two commonly exploited fungal species and state how they are used:

   (a) _____

   (b) _____

Microorganisms & Biotechnology

Code: RA 1

Techniques in Microbial Culture

Bacteria and fungi may be cultured in liquid or solid media. These comprise a base of **agar** to which is added the nutrients required for microbial growth. Agar is a gelatinous colloidal extract of red algae, and can be used in solid or liquid form. It is used because of its two unique physical properties. Firstly, it melts at 100°C and remains liquid until cooled to 40°C, at which point it gels. Secondly, few microbes are capable of digesting agar so the medium is not used up during culture. The addition of microbes to an agar plate, or to liquid agar, is called **inoculation** and must be carried out under aseptic conditions. **Aseptic techniques** involve the **sterilisation** of equipment and culture media to prevent cross contamination by unwanted microbes. Sterilisation is a process by which all organisms and spores are destroyed, either by heat or by chemicals.

Conditions for the Culture of Bacteria and Fungi

Fungi

Temperature: Most fungi have an optimum temperature for growth of 25°C, but most are adapted to survive between 5 and 35°C.

pH: Fungi prefer a neutral (pH 7) growing environment, although most species can tolerate slightly acidic conditions.

Nutrients: Fungi require a source of carbon and nitrogen to produce protein. They also require trace elements such as potassium, phosphorus and magnesium. Growth factors can be added to increase the rate of fungal growth.

Water potential: Fungi are 85-90% water by mass. Water is constantly lost from the hyphae via evaporation and must be replaced through absorption from the media. To aid water uptake, media have a water potential that is less negative than that of the fungal tissue.

Gaseous environment: The majority of fungi are aerobic and very few species can tolerate anaerobic conditions. This is why fungi always grow on the surface of a culture medium, not inside it.

Bacteria

Temperature: Most bacteria cultured in the school laboratory are classified as **mesophiles**. Mesophiles prefer temperatures between 20 and 40°C.

pH: Most bacteria grow optimally in media with a pH between 6 and 8. Very few bacteria can grow in acidic conditions.

Nutrients: Bacteria need a source of carbon, nitrogen and mineral salts as raw ingredients for cellular growth.

Water potential: All bacteria require water for growth. To prevent cell lysis or dehydration, the water potential of the medium must be such that net water fluxes into and out of the bacterial cell are minimised.

Gaseous environment: Aerobic bacteria will grow only in oxygenated environments, whereas obligate anaerobes (e.g. *Clostridium*) do not tolerate oxygen. Facultative anaerobes grow under aerobic conditions, but are able to metabolise anaerobically when oxygen is unavailable. All bacterial cultures benefit from a low concentration of carbon dioxide.

Inoculating Solid Media

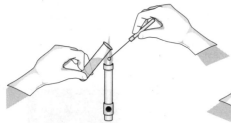  

1. Hold the inoculating loop in the flame until it glows red hot. Remove the lid from the culture broth and pass the neck of the bottle through the flame.

2. Dip the cool inoculating loop into the broth. Flame the neck of the bottle again and replace the lid.

3. Raise the lid of the plate just enough to allow the loop to streak the plate. Streak the surface of the media. Seal the plate with tape and incubate upside down.

1. Explain why inoculated plates must be stored upside down in an incubator: _____

_____

2. Outline the correct procedure for the disposal of microbial plates and cultures: _____

_____

3. Suggest a general method by which you could separate microorganisms through culturing: _____

_____

Strain Isolation

In nature, bacteria exist as mixed populations. However, in order to study them in the laboratory they must exist as pure cultures (i.e. cultures in which all organisms are descendants of the same organism or clones). The most common way of separating bacterial cells on the agar surface is the **streak plate method**. This provides a simple and rapid method of diluting the sample by mechanical means. As the loop is streaked across the agar surface, more and more bacteria are rubbed off until individual separated organisms are deposited on the agar. After incubation, the area at the beginning of the streak pattern will show **confluent** growth (growth as a continuous sheet), while the area near the end of the pattern should show discrete colonies. Isolated colonies can then be removed from the streak plate using aseptic techniques, and transferred to new sterile medium. After incubation, all organisms in the new culture will be descendants of the same organism (i.e. a pure culture).

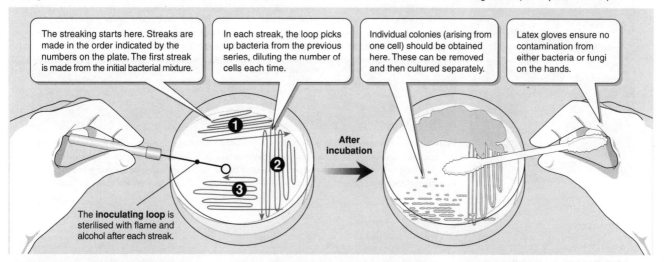

The streaking starts here. Streaks are made in the order indicated by the numbers on the plate. The first streak is made from the initial bacterial mixture.

In each streak, the loop picks up bacteria from the previous series, diluting the number of cells each time.

Individual colonies (arising from one cell) should be obtained here. These can be removed and then cultured separately.

Latex gloves ensure no contamination from either bacteria or fungi on the hands.

After incubation

The **inoculating loop** is sterilised with flame and alcohol after each streak.

When approximately 10 to 100 million bacterial cells are present, colonies become visible. Note the well-isolated colonies in the photo above. A single colony may be removed for further investigation.

A swab containing a single strain of bacteria is used to inoculate additional nutrient plates to produce pure cultures of bacteria (clones).

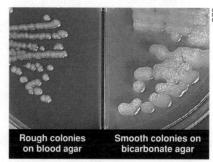

Rough colonies on blood agar

Smooth colonies on bicarbonate agar

To test purity, a sample of a culture can be grown on a selective medium that promotes the growth of a single species. The photo above shows a positive encapsulation test for *Bacillus anthracis*.

Microorganisms & Biotechnology

1. Explain the basis by which bacteria are isolated using streak plating: _____

_____

2 Discuss the basic principles of aseptic technique, outlining why each procedure is necessary: _____

_____

_____

_____

_____

3. Comment on the importance of aseptic (sterile) technique in streak plating: _____

_____

_____

4. State how many bacterial cells must be present on the plate before the colony becomes visible to the naked eye:

_____

5. Outline when it might be necessary to use **selective media** to culture bacteria: _____

_____

Serial Dilution

The growth of microorganisms in culture can be measured in a number of ways. Some indirect methods measure culture dry weight or turbidity, both of which are often directly proportional to cell density. More commonly used are methods that directly or indirectly count the number of cells in a culture. Microbial populations are often very large, so most counting methods rely on counting a very small sample of the culture. A commonly used indirect method is serial dilution followed by plate counts (below). If care is taken with the serial dilution, this method can provide a relatively accurate estimate of culture density.

Measuring Microbial Growth Using Serial Dilution

Serial dilution can be performed at different stages during the culture growth. By making a series of dilutions and then counting the colonies that arise after plating, the density of the original inoculum (starting culture) can be calculated. Colonies should be well separated and the number of colonies counted should ideally be neither too small nor too large (about 15-30 is good).

CALCULATION: No. of colonies on plate X reciprocal of sample dilution = no. of bacteria per cm^3.

EXAMPLE: 28 colonies on a plate of 1/1000 dilution, then the original culture contained:

$28 \times 1000 = 28 \times 10^3\ cm^{-3}$ bacterial cells

Plate counts are widely used in microbiology. It is a useful technique because only the viable colonies are counted, but it requires some incubation time before colonies form. For quality control purposes in some food industries where the food product is perishable (e.g. milk processing) this time delay is unacceptable and direct methods (e.g. cell counts using oil immersion microscopy) are used.

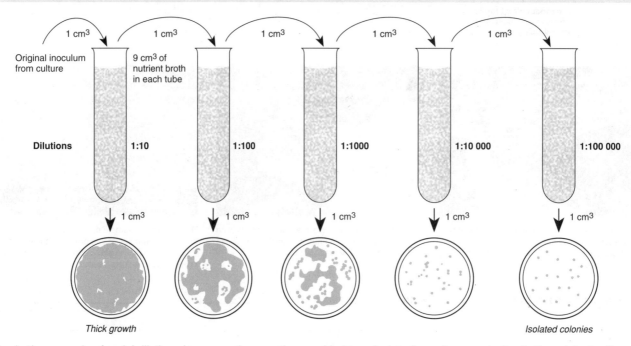

1. In the example of serial dilution above, use the equation provided to calculate the cell concentration in the original culture:

_____

2. (a) Explain the term **viable count**: _____

_____

(b) Explain why dilution plating is a useful technique for obtaining a viable count:_____

_____

_____

(c) Investigate an alternative technique, such as turbidimetry and identify how the technique differs from dilution plating:

_____

_____

_____

_____

Uses of Microorganisms

Bacteria and fungi are used extensively in many aspects of biotechnology. Microorganisms have traditionally been used in the production of fermented foods: alcoholic beverages, bread, and fermented dairy products. The control and efficiency of these uses have been greatly refined in recent times. Newer applications of microbes include their use in the production of alternative fuels (e.g. biogas and gasohol), enzymes, pharmaceuticals, and in sewage treatment. The advent of genetic engineering has increased the range of microbial products available and has provided alternative sources for products that were once available only through expensive or wasteful means (e.g. production of the enzyme rennin). Future applications include the wider use of genetically engineered microbes in crop improvement and as biological pesticides.

Microorganisms in the Food Industry

Cheese production uses cultures of lactic acid bacteria (e.g. *Streptococcus* spp.) and genetically engineered microbial rennin, which is added to curd the milk protein. Microbial activity occurs at several stages to produce characteristic flavours and textures.

Yoghurt is produced from milk by the action of lactic acid bacteria particularly *Lactobacillus bulgaricus* and *Streptococcus thermophilus*. These bacteria break down milk proteins into peptides.

Soy sauce (shoyu): Filamentous fungi (*Aspergillus soyae* and *A.oryzeae*) digest soy proteins and solids. The culture is fermented in the presence of lactic acid bacteria (*Lactobacillus* spp.) and acid tolerant yeast (e.g. *Torulopsis*) over a year or more.

Bread (leavened): The sugars in the dough are fermented by the yeast, *Saccharomyces cerevisiae*, producing alcohol and CO_2. The gas causes the dough to rise, while the alcohol is converted to flavour compounds during baking.

Beer and wine: The sugars in fruits (wine) or grains (beers) are fermented by yeast (e.g. *Saccharomyces carlsbergensis, S. cerevisiae*) to alcohol. Beer production first requires a malting process to convert starches in the grain to fermentable sugars.

Sauerkraut production involves the fermentation of cabbage. The initial fermentation involves lactic acid bacteria (*Leuconostoc mesenteroides* and *Enterobacter cloacae*), followed by acid production with *Lactobacillus plantarum*.

Vinegar production uses cultures of acetic acid bacteria (e.g. *Acetobacter* and *Gluconobacter*). When you leave wine exposed to oxygen, these bacteria convert the alcoholic brew (ethanol) to ethanoic acid (vinegar).

Vitamins and amino acids are dietary supplements produced as by-products of faulty or altered microbial metabolism. Examples include lysine and vitamin B_{12}. Microbial species used include: *Corynebacterium glutamicum, Pseudomonas, Propionibacterium*.

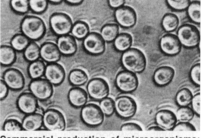

Commercial production of microorganisms: Baker's yeast (*Saccharomyces cerevisiae*, above) is sold for both industrial use and home brewing and baking. *Bacillus thuringiensis* is a widely used biological pest control agent. Nitrogen fixing bacteria (e.g. *Rhizobium*) are used to enhance plant nutrition.

1. (a) Explain what is meant by the term **industrial microbiology**: _____

_____

(b) State one application of industrial microbiology: _____

(c) Explain why industrial microbiology is an important field of science: _____

_____

_____

_____

Microorganisms & Biotechnology

Uses of Microorganisms in Medicine and the Environment

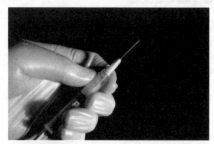

Human proteins: Many human proteins are made by microbial fermentation. Genetic engineering has enabled many of these proteins to be obtained from non-animal sources. For instance, human insulin can now be made from genetically engineered yeast (*Saccharomyces cerevisiae*) or *E. coli*.

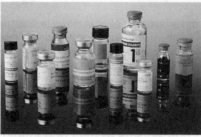

Antibiotics and pharmaceuticals: These are produced as by-products of microbial metabolism using fermentation technology. Examples include antibiotics from *Penicillium* and *Streptomyces* spp., oestrogen (for contraception), cortisone (as an anti-inflammatory).

Bioremediation: Bacteria (e.g. *Pseudomonas* spp.) metabolise the hydrocarbons in oil spills, breaking down the oil into its basic constituents.

Metal mining: Bacteria (e.g. *Thiobacillus ferrooxidans*) are used in the recovery of metals from otherwise unprofitable grades of uranium and copper ores.

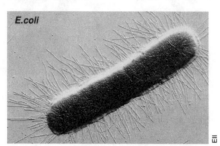

E.coli

Environmental biosensors: Bacteria (e.g. *Vibrio fischeri, Lactococcus, Photobacterium, E.coli*) can be genetically engineered to detect specific pollutants. The pollutant may activate a light-emitting compound in the bacterium, which can be easily detected.

Sewage treatment: Bacterial activity (e.g. *Zoogloea* bacteria) produces flocculant masses (floc), oxidising organic matter to CO_2 and water.

2. Briefly describe two examples of how microorganisms are used in each of the following applications:

   (a) Production of alcoholic beverages: _____

   _____

   _____

   (b) Environmental monitoring and clean-up: _____

   _____

   _____

   (c) Agricultural crop improvement and protection: _____

   _____

   _____

3. Outline how genetically engineered bacteria can be used in:

   (a) The detection of pollutants: _____

   _____

   _____

   (b) The production of human proteins: _____

   _____

   _____

4. Describe one example of how genetic engineering has improved the efficiency of traditional biotechnologies:

   _____

   _____

   _____

Energy Resources

There is a global energy crisis looming. The combined effect of the dwindling reserves of fossil fuels, combined with their rather catastrophic long term effect on the world's climate, make the search for renewable energy sources imperative. Alternative energy sources such as solar power and the requisite high efficiency batteries have yet to become efficient enough and cheap enough to be serious replacements for fossil fuels.

Renewable biomass energy resources may provide a useful supplement to traditional fuels such as **coal**, **gas**, and **oil** (including its refined products of diesel, petrol, and kerosene). **Biofuels** include ethanol, **gasohol** (a blend of petrol and ethanol), methanol, and diesel made from a blend of plant oils and traditional diesel oil. **Biogas** (methane) is an important renewable gas fuel made by fermenting wastes in a digester.

Gasohol

Gasohol is a blend of finished motor gasoline containing alcohol (generally ethanol but sometimes methanol). In Brazil, gasohol consists of 24% ethanol mixed with petrol.

Advantages
- Cleaner fuel than petrol
- Renewable resource
- Creates many jobs in rural areas

Disadvantages
- Ethanol burns hotter than petrol so petrol engines tend to overheat and they need to be modified
- Fuel tank and pipes need coating to prevent corrosion by ethanol
- Fuel consumption 20% greater compared with petrol

Sources of biomass for ethanol production
- *Sugar cane* (ethanol is produced in this way in Brazil).
- *Corn starch* (in the USA).
- Grass, certain waste materials (paper, cardboard), and from wood. Fast-growing hardwood trees can be treated to release cellulose. Once released, it may be converted to simple glucose by hydrolytic enzymes and then fermented to produce ethanol.

Biogas

Methane gas is produced by anaerobic fermentation of organic wastes such as sewage sludge at sewage waste treatment stations, animal dung, agricultural wastes, or by the rotting contents of landfill sites.

Stages in methane production

Saprophytic bacteria (facultative anaerobes) break down fats, proteins, and polysaccharides.

↓

Acid-forming bacteria break down these monomers to short-chain organic acids.

↓

Methanogen bacteria (strict anaerobes) produce methane gas.

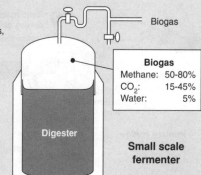

Biogas

Biogas
Methane: 50-80%
CO_2: 15-45%
Water: 5%

Digester

Small scale fermenter

Sources: *Biological Sciences Review*, Sep 2000, pp.27-29; *Biologist*, Feb 1998, pp. 17-21; Microorganism & Biotechnology, 1997, Chenn, P. (John Murray Publishers).

Traditional sources of renewable energy include animal dung, which is collected and then dried in the sun and used as fuel.

Fuels such as petrol, diesel, LPG, and CNG are derived from oil and natural gas extracted from non-renewable geological deposits.

Coal provided the energy for the industrial revolution. It is now regarded as a dirty fuel with many health hazards associated with its use.

1. Explain the nature of the following renewable fuels:

(a) Biogas: _____

_____

(b) Gasohol: _____

_____

2. Name the sources of biomass that are commonly used for the production of ethanol fuel: _____

_____

3. List two disadvantages of using pure ethanol as a motor fuel: _____

_____

4. Suggest how a small biogas fermenter may be used on a farm in the UK to reduce waste and provide a fuel source:

_____

_____

_____

Microorganisms & Biotechnology

Code: DA 2

Sewage Treatment

Once water has been used by household or industry, it becomes sewage. Sewage includes toilet wastes and all household water, but excludes storm water, which is usually diverted directly into waterways. In some cities, the sewerage and stormwater systems may be partly combined, and sewage can overflow into surface water during high rainfall. When sewage reaches a treatment plant, it can undergo up to three levels of processing (purification). Primary treatment is little more than a mechanical screening process, followed by settling of the solids into a sludge. Secondary sewage treatment is primarily a biological process in which aerobic and anaerobic microorganisms are used to remove the organic wastes. Advanced secondary treatment targets specific pollutants, particularly nitrates, phosphates, and heavy metals. Before water is discharged after treatment, it is always disinfected (usually by chlorination) to kill bacteria and other potential pathogens.

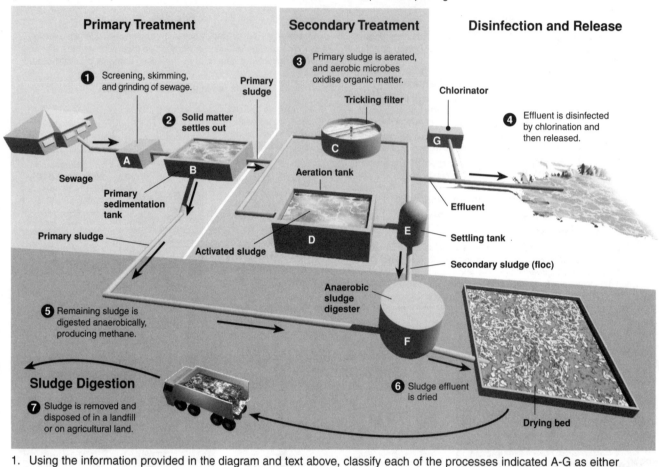

Primary Treatment

1 Screening, skimming, and grinding of sewage.

2 Solid matter settles out

Sewage

A

B

Primary sedimentation tank

Primary sludge

Secondary Treatment

Primary sludge

3 Primary sludge is aerated, and aerobic microbes oxidise organic matter.

Trickling filter

C

Aeration tank

D

Activated sludge

E

Anaerobic sludge digester

F

Disinfection and Release

Chlorinator

G

4 Effluent is disinfected by chlorination and then released.

Effluent

Settling tank

Secondary sludge (floc)

5 Remaining sludge is digested anaerobically, producing methane.

Sludge Digestion

7 Sludge is removed and disposed of in a landfill or on agricultural land.

6 Sludge effluent is dried

Drying bed

1. Using the information provided in the diagram and text above, classify each of the processes indicated A-G as either mechanical, biological, or chemical. If you wish, colour code these on the diagram for easy reference:

   A: _____   D: _____   G: _____

   B: _____   E: _____

   C: _____   F: _____

2. Using the diagram above for reference, investigate the sewage treatment process in your own town or city, identifying the specific techniques and problems of waste water management in your area. Make a note of the main points to cover in the space provided below, and develop your discussion as a separate report. Identify:

   (a) Your urban area and treatment station: _____

   (b) The volume of sewage processed: _____

   (c) The degree of purification: _____

   (d) The treatment processes used (list): _____

   (e) The discharge point(s): _____

   (f) Problems of waste water management: _____

   _____

   (g) Future options or plans: _____

   _____

Industrial Microbiology

Industrial production of microbial products involves large scale culture of fungi and bacteria to produce commercially valuable substances. Many pharmaceuticals and food ingredients (flavourings, thickeners, stabilisers, and enzymes) are produced using these microbial fermentations. The microbes are first **isolated** and then cultured in an appropriate environment. The desired product is then extracted from the cells themselves (e.g. enzymes) or from the culture medium (e.g. antibiotics). While it is relatively easy to grow microbes on a small scale, **scaling** up these procedures for use on an industrial scale creates numerous problems. **Bioreactors** optimise the conditions for microbial growth and production of the desired product. Many of the microbes used in industry produce valuable commodities as by-products of their normal metabolism. Others are natural mutants with faulty metabolic pathways, and some are genetically engineered to express a particular gene as its protein product. (See previous pages for information on techniques in microbial culture).

Industrial Fermenter (Bioreactor) Technology

PHOTO: Bioengineering AG (Switzerland)

The photograph above shows an industrial scale bioreactor used for the production of diphtheria and pertussis vaccine. The types of microorganisms that are well suited to use in industry show certain properties: they have simple nutritional requirements, temperature and pH optima for maximum growth, amenability to culture in large scale fermenters, and a high growth rate (therefore high productivity).

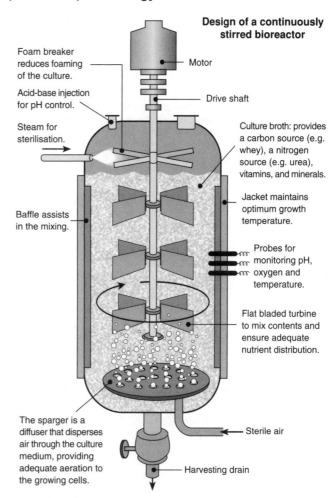

Design of a continuously stirred bioreactor

Foam breaker reduces foaming of the culture.

Acid-base injection for pH control.

Steam for sterilisation.

Baffle assists in the mixing.

Motor

Drive shaft

Culture broth: provides a carbon source (e.g. whey), a nitrogen source (e.g. urea), vitamins, and minerals.

Jacket maintains optimum growth temperature.

Probes for monitoring pH, oxygen and temperature.

Flat bladed turbine to mix contents and ensure adequate nutrient distribution.

The sparger is a diffuser that disperses air through the culture medium, providing adequate aeration to the growing cells.

Sterile air

Harvesting drain

Microorganisms & Biotechnology

The Problems Associated With Scaling Up

Effective scaling up of relatively simple laboratory procedures to full sized industrial biofermenters requires microbiologists and bioengineers to solve a number of problems:

- All undesirable organisms must be prevented from entering the fermenter. There can be no risk of contamination.

- Cultures of aerobic microbes must be given an adequate supply of oxygen. This can be difficult in large volume cultures.

- Powerful motors are needed to mix the culture which has a porridge like consistency.

- Nutrient levels need to be maintained at optimum levels throughout the life of the culture.

- The heat generated by microbial activity needs to dissipated. The entire culture must be keep at a constant temperature.

- Waste products need to be constantly removed.

- The build up of foam due to the production of carbon dioxide must be monitored and controlled.

- Rigorous testing using scale models (*left*) must be carried out to ensure that the problems associated with scaling up have been eliminated.

Patterns of Microbial Growth and Production of Metabolites

Graph A

Log phase: Exponential growth due to high metabolic activity and cellular reproduction rate. Cells are most vulnerable to adverse conditions and anti-microbial agents.

Lag phase: Cells increase in size and synthesise enzymes, but there is little or no cell division

Stationary phase: Growth rate slows and the population stabilises

Death phase: Microbial deaths exceed the numbers produced

Primary metabolite: Produced by metabolic activity essential for cell survival (e.g. respiration)

Weight or log 10 of cell numbers

Time

—— Yeast growth

······ Ethanol production

Graph A: Phases of microbial growth and production of a primary metabolite
When the number of organisms in a culture is plotted against time, the curve typically shows four phases (indicated above). Primary metabolites (e.g. ethanol) are formed at the same time as the cells and therefore the production and growth curves are similar.

Graph B

Penicillin

Mould

Secondary metabolite: Metabolic by-products not essential to immediate survival. Most yield occurs at the end of the active growth period

Growth slows and the secondary metabolite may be harvested

Weight

Time

Graph B: Production of a secondary metabolite
Secondary metabolites, such as penicillin, are not produced until the microbe has largely completed its growth and has entered the stationary phase.

1. (a) Explain why there is an initial lag in the growth of a microorganism placed into a new culture: _____

_____

   (b) Suggest how this time lag could be reduced when starting new culture: _____

_____

2. Distinguish between a primary and secondary metabolite in microbial culture: _____

_____

_____

3. Continuous (as opposed to batch) culture systems, remove culture and replenish the medium during culture growth:

   (a) Explain why continuous culture techniques are often used when the actual cells themselves (or their primary metabolites) are being harvested industrially:

_____

_____

   (b) Explain when batch culture (with final harvest of the end-product) would be used in preference to continuous culture:

_____

_____

4. Outline how industrial biofermenters overcome the following problems associated with scaling up:

   (a) Heat generated by microbial activity: _____

_____

   (b) Microbial demand for oxygen: _____

_____

   (c) Foam generation: _____

_____

   (d) Nutrient demand: _____

_____

Industrial Production of Enzymes

Humans have used enzymes for thousands of years in food and beverage production, but the use of enzymes in industry is a comparatively recent development. Many industries now rely on the large scale production of microbial enzymes to catalyse a range of reactions. In the absence of enzymes, these reactions sometimes require high temperatures or pressures to proceed. Industrial enzymes must be relatively robust against denaturation and capable of maintaining activity over a wide temperature and pH range. Enzyme technology involves the production, isolation, purification, and application of useful enzymes. Commercial enzymes are produced from three main

sources: plants, animals, and microorganisms (mainly bacteria and fungi). Most enzymes used in industrial processes today are microbial in origin and are produced in industrial-scale microbial fermentations using liquid or semi-solid growth media. Note that the term **fermentation**, when used in reference to industrial microbiology, applies to both aerobic and anaerobic microbial growth in **bioreactors**. Generalised plans for the industrial production of both extracellular and intracellular enzymes are illustrated below. Note that the isolation of intracellular enzymes (below, right) is more complex because the cells must first be disrupted to release the enzymes within.

1 **Growth of the microorganisms:**
A closed fermenter system is an enclosed, **sterile system** containing culture broth in which the microorganisms (bacteria or fungi) are grown until the extracellular products (or the cells themselves) have accumulated for harvesting. Conditions in the fermenter vessel are closely monitored and carefully regulated so that the conditions for maximal microbial growth are optimised.

The model (right) shows a cutaway section of a cylindrical fermentation chamber, typical of that used for continuous microbial cultures.

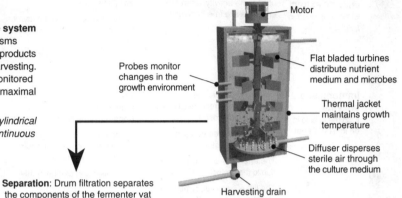

Motor

Probes monitor changes in the growth environment

Flat bladed turbines distribute nutrient medium and microbes

Thermal jacket maintains growth temperature

Diffuser disperses sterile air through the culture medium

Harvesting drain

2 **Separation:** Drum filtration separates the components of the fermenter vat

Producing Extracellular Enzymes

Culture medium and secreted (extracellular) enzymes

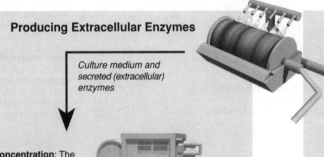

3 **Concentration:** The enzyme solution is concentrated by reducing its water content, e.g. by **reverse osmosis**.

Preservation: Antibacterial agents are added at this stage to prevent contamination.

3a ┈┈▶ Crude product

4 **Purification and processing:** The crude enzyme product may be dried to produce a powder or further purified by precipitation, crystallisation or **adsorption** (e.g. on to clays).

Producing Intracellular Enzymes

Microbial cells and the enzymes contained within them

3 **Disruption:** Once the cells have been separated from the culture medium, they must be disrupted (using ultrasound) to release the enzymes within the cells.

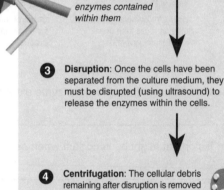

4 **Centrifugation:** The cellular debris remaining after disruption is removed by centrifugation (or filtration).

5 **Purification and processing:** Initial purification involves precipitation with ammonium sulfate or organic solvents. Further purification occurs by **ion exchange chromatography** or gel electrophoresis.

1. The industrial production of microbial enzymes varies according to the enzyme involved and its desired end use. Compare the two flow diagrams, for intracellular and extracellular enzymes, above:

   (a) Explain the main way in which the two production methods differ: _____

   _____

   (b) Suggest the reason for this difference: _____

   _____

2. Enzyme solutions can be packaged and used as crude extracts without further purification (3a). State one benefit of this:

   _____

Putting Enzymes to Use

Depending on the way in which the desired end-product is produced, enzymes may be used as crude whole cell preparations or as cell-free enzyme extracts. Whole cell preparations are cost effective, and appropriate when the processes involved in production of the end product are complex, as in waste treatment and the production of semi-synthetic antibiotics. Cell free enzyme extracts are more expensive to produce, but can be a more efficient option overall. To reduce costs and improve the efficiency of product production, enzymes are sometimes immobilised within a matrix of some kind and the reactants are passed over them. The various methods by which enzymes are put to work are compared in the diagram below.

Industrial enzymes

	Advantages	Disadvantages	Methods of Enzyme Immobilisation
Cell free enzyme extract Enzyme is used in solution	There is generally a high level of enzyme activity when the enzymes are free in solution.	The enzyme may be washed away after use. The end-product is not enzyme free and may require purification.	**Micro-encapsulation** The enzyme is held within a membrane, or within alginate or polyacrylamide capsules. *Partially permeable membrane*
Immobilised enzyme Enzyme is held in an inert material	The enzymes can be used repeatedly and recovered easily (this reduces costs). The enzyme-free end-product is easily harvested. The enzymes are more stable due to the protection of a matrix. The life of some enzymes, e.g. proteases, is extended by immobilisation.	The entrapment process may reduce the enzyme activity (more enzyme will be needed). Some methods offering high stability (e.g. covalent bonding) are harder to achieve. Immobilisation can be costly.	**Lattice entrapment** Enzyme is trapped in a gel lattice, e.g. silica gel. The substrate and reaction products diffuse in and out of the matrix. *Enzymes trapped in a gel lattice* **Covalent attachment** Enzyme is covalently bonded to a solid surface e.g. collagen or a synthetic polymer. *Enzyme* *Substrate, e.g. collagen*
Whole cell preparation Whole cells may be immobilised	Useful for enzymes that are unstable or inactivated when outside the cell. Useful for complex processes utilising more than one intracellular enzyme.	Less expensive and more rapid than first producing a pure enzyme extract. Some of the substrate is used for microbial growth, so the process is less efficient overall.	*Glutaraldehyde* **Direct cross-linking** Glutaraldehyde is used to cross-link the enzymes. They then precipitate out and are immobilised without support.

1. (a) Explain one benefit of using a cell free enzyme extract to produce a high-value end-product:

_____

(b) Identify one factor that might be important when deciding *not* to use a cell free extract: _____

_____

2. (a) Describe two benefits of using immobilised enzymes (rather than enzymes in solution) for industrial processes:

_____

_____

(b) Describe a disadvantage associated with the use of immobilised enzymes: _____

_____

(c) Describe a factor that would affect the rate of end-product harvest from immobilised enzymes:

_____

3. The useful life of protease enzymes is extended when they are immobilised (as opposed to being in solution). Using what you know of enzyme structure, explain why immobilisation has this effect in this case:

_____

_____

4. Suggest why immobilisation would reduce the activity of certain enzymes: _____

_____

_____

Applications of Enzymes

Microbes are ideal organisms for the industrial production of enzymes because of their high productivity, ease of culture in industrial fermenters, and the ease with which they can be genetically modified to produce particular products. In addition, because there is an enormous diversity in microbial metabolism, the variety of enzymes available for exploitation is very large. Some of the microorganisms involved in industrial fermentations, and their enzymes and their applications are described below.

Enzymes are used in various stages of **cheese production**, e.g. chymosin from GE microbes now replaces the rennin previously obtained from calves.

In **beer brewing**, **proteases** (from bacteria) are added to prevent cloudiness. Amyloglucosidases are used to produce low calorie beers.

Citric acid is used in jam production and is synthesised by a mutant strain of the fungus *Aspergillus niger*, which produces the enzyme citrate synthase.

Biological detergents use **proteases**, **lipases**, and **amylases** extracted from fungi and thermophilic bacteria to break down organic material in stains.

Fungal ligninases are used in **pulp and paper industries** to remove lignin from wood pulp and treat wood waste.

Medical treatment of blood clots employs protease enzymes such as streptokinase from *Streptomyces* spp.

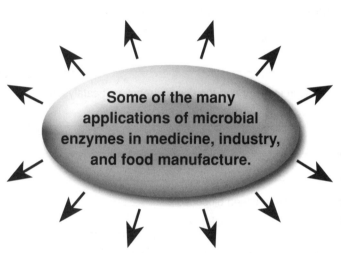

Some of the many applications of microbial enzymes in medicine, industry, and food manufacture.

In **soft centred chocolates**, **invertase** from yeast breaks down the solid filling to produce the soft centre.

Bacterial proteases are used to break down the wheat protein (gluten) in flour, to produce low gluten breads.

Cellulases and pectinases are used in the manufacture of packaged (as opposed to fresh) fruit juices to speed juice extraction and prevent cloudiness.

The silver residues from old photographs can be reclaimed for reuse when proteases are employed to digest the gelatin of old films.

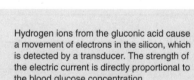

The lactase from bacteria is used to convert lactose to glucose and galactose in the production of low-lactose and lactose free milk products.

Tanning industries now use proteases from *Bacillus subtilis* instead of toxic chemicals, such as sulfide pastes, to remove hairs and soften hides.

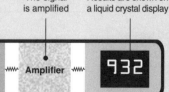

Microorganisms & Biotechnology

The enzyme, **glucose oxidase**, from *Aspergillus niger*, is immobilised in a semi-conducting silicon chip. It catalyses the conversion of glucose (from the blood sample) to gluconic acid.

Hydrogen ions from the gluconic acid cause a movement of electrons in the silicon, which is detected by a transducer. The strength of the electric current is directly proportional to the blood glucose concentration.

Plastic sleeve | Membrane permeable to glucose | The signal is amplified | Results are shown on a liquid crystal display

Biological recognition layer | Transducer | Amplifier | 932

Biosensors are electronic monitoring devices that use biological material to detect the presence or concentration of a particular substance. Enzymes are ideally suited for use in biosensors because of their specificity and sensitivity. This example illustrates how **glucose oxidase** from the fungus *Aspergillus niger* is used in a biosensor to measure blood glucose level in diabetics.

1. Identify two probable consequences of the absence of enzymes from a chemical reaction that normally uses them:

   (a) _____

   (b) _____

2. Identify three properties of microbial enzymes that make them highly suitable as industrial catalysts. For each, explain why the property is important:

   (a) _____

   _____

   (b) _____

   _____

   (c) _____

   _____

3. Choose one example from those described in the diagram opposite and, in more detail, identify:

   (a) The enzyme and its specific microbial source: _____

   _____

   (b) The application of the enzyme in industry and the specific reaction it catalyses: _____

   _____

   _____

   _____

4. (a) Outline the basic principle of enzyme-based biosensors: _____

   _____

   (b) Suggest how a biosensor could be used to monitor blood alcohol level: _____

   _____

   _____

   _____

5. For each of the examples described below, suggest how the use of microbial enzymes has improved the efficiency, cost effectiveness, and/or safety of processing compared with traditional methods:

   (a) Use of microbial proteases to treat hides in the tanning industry: _____

   _____

   _____

   _____

   (b) Use of microbial chymosin in cheese production: _____

   _____

   _____

   _____

   (c) Use of fungal ligninases to treat wood waste: _____

   _____

   _____

   _____

White Wine Production

Yeasts are involved in producing almost all alcoholic beverages: wines, beers, and distilled spirits such as rum and whisky. The alcohol produced in the manufacture of these beverages is a metabolic by-product of **fermentation** by the yeast. Wines are made from grapes, which contain sugars that are directly available to the yeast for fermentation. There are literally hundreds of different variations on the wine making process. The colour of wine is not determined by the juice of the grape, which is usually clear, but by the presence or absence of the grape skin during fermentation. White wine can be made from any colour of grape as the skins are separated from the juice. The steps in the manufacturing white wine are illustrated below.

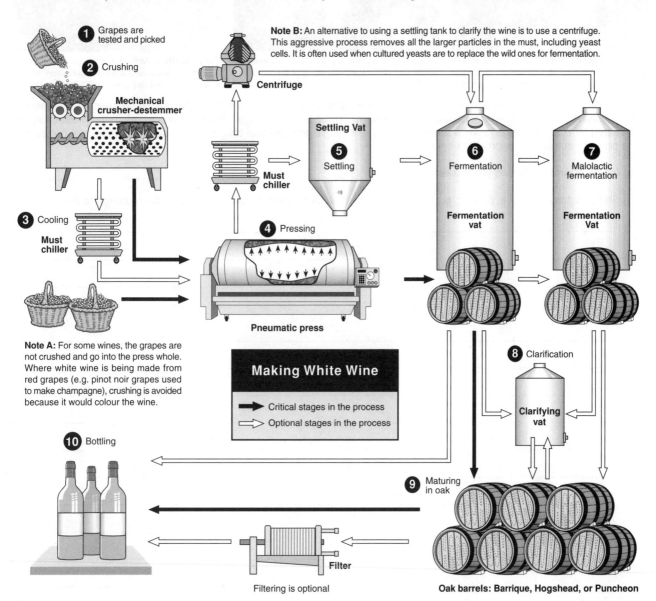

Note B: An alternative to using a settling tank to clarify the wine is to use a centrifuge. This aggressive process removes all the larger particles in the must, including yeast cells. It is often used when cultured yeasts are to replace the wild ones for fermentation.

1 Grapes are tested and picked

2 Crushing

Mechanical crusher-destemmer

Centrifuge

3 Cooling

Must chiller

Must chiller

Settling Vat

5 Settling

4 Pressing

Pneumatic press

6 Fermentation

Fermentation vat

7 Malolactic fermentation

Fermentation Vat

8 Clarification

Clarifying vat

Note A: For some wines, the grapes are not crushed and go into the press whole. Where white wine is being made from red grapes (e.g. pinot noir grapes used to make champagne), crushing is avoided because it would colour the wine.

Making White Wine

➡ Critical stages in the process

⇨ Optional stages in the process

10 Bottling

9 Maturing in oak

Filter

Filtering is optional

Oak barrels: Barrique, Hogshead, or Puncheon

Microorganisms & Biotechnology

1. Grapes are tested for acidity and sugar levels before picking.

2. Before crushing, the grapes are separated from the leaves and stems. Crushing produces 'must'; a mix of skins and juice. Sulfite may be added at this stage. This dissipates before the fermentation stage (see Note **A** above).

3. If warm weather makes the temperature of the must too high, the juice is cooled by pumping it through 'must chillers'. Delaying fermentation until after pressing is essential.

4. White wine grapes are always pressed. Modern pneumatic presses (illustrated above) prevent pips and stems breaking; something that could add bitter flavours to the wine (important to avoid in white wine).

5. The juice is drained into settling vats where the pip, stem and skin fragments settle to the bottom of the vat. The clean juice is racked into separate vats ready for fermentation (see Note **B** above).

6. The traditional oak casks used for fermentation are being increasingly replaced by stainless steel vats which enable better control of yeast activity through temperature regulation. Most often, a cultured yeast *Saccharomyces cerevisiae* is added, although some winemakers

choose to use the wild yeasts present on the skin of the grapes. The yeast ferments the sugars present in the grape juice.

7. A second, **malolactic** fermentation may occur naturally or may be induced to soften acidic flavours and add complexity to the wine. This fermentation, carried out by bacteria and not yeast, converts the harsher malic acid into softer lactic ones.

8. After fermentation of the juice, the wine is stabilised by filtration, centrifuging, or *fining* in a **clarification vat** with a small amount of a bentonite clay (which collects remaining yeasts, proteins and grape particles, and precipitates them to the bottom of the vat). If not removed, protein can cause cloudiness in the finished wine. Bitartrates are removed by chilling the wine. If left in the wine, they cause crystal formation when it is chilled, although they are harmless and tasteless.

9. Some wines are bottled after chilling, but wines requiring further development undergo maturation in oak barrels (e.g. chardonnay).

10. Because wines are susceptible to air and bacteria, the bottles are sterilised and filled in the absence of air. Bottled wines requiring further maturation are cellared before commercial release.

Picking: Grapes can be picked by hand or with mechanical harvesters. The harvesters shake the vines and ripe grapes drop on to a conveyer belt.

Pressing: The wine is pressed to remove the solids and separate the wine. It is then clarified in a series of settling vats.

Fermentation: After the addition of the yeast *Saccharomyces cerevisae*, fermentation occurs in stainless steel tanks, grouped into 'tank farms'.

1. Using the information above and on the previous page for guidance, investigate the wine making process for a named white wine. Note that in the generalised diagram shown on the previous page, obligatory processes in the production are indicated by black arrows and white arrows indicate alternative or additional stages. Summarise the important points in the process in the spaces provided below:

(a) Name of white wine and winemaker (if relevant): _____

(b) Steps in production (i.e. picking, pressing, settling, fermenting, fining, bottling), including the reasons for these:

(c) Special features of the process for this example: _____

Red Wine Production

Red wine is made from red (or black) grapes, but its red colour is bestowed by the skin being left in contact with the juice during fermentation. The grape varieties used for red wines vary tremendously in their characteristics, most importantly colour, flavour, and tannins. Many of the basic steps in red wine production are similar to those outlined for making white wines (see the previous activity), but there are important differences related to the extent of crushing, pressing (grapes are always pressed in white wine production), maceration, and alternative fermentation processes.

Harvest: The condition of the grapes at the time of harvest is crucial to wine quality. Overripe or underripe grapes have too much or too little sugar and this affects alcohol content and wine quality.

Vine trimming: This is done to improve the light penetration to the grapes. It can carried out at various stages during the growing season and may be done by hand or using machines.

Destemming is a mechanical process that occurs immediately prior to crushing. Although it is not always necessary, destemming prevents excessive tannins in the wine.

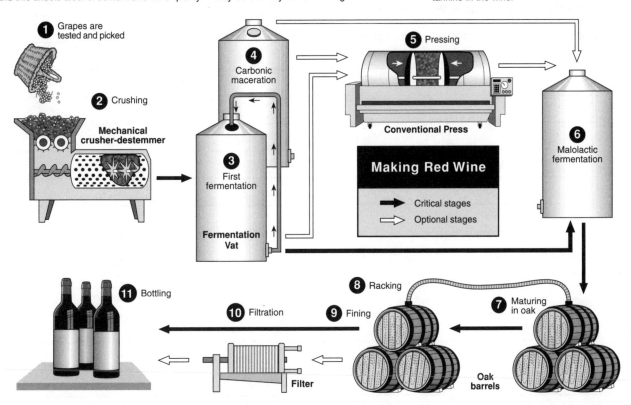

1. Grapes are tested and picked as for white wine production.

2. The grapes are **crushed** and **destemmed**. Destemming is not always necessary and bunches may be crushed whole. Stems are removed if the winemaker wishes to avoid high levels of tannin in the wine.

3. While many red wines are still fermented in vats made of oak, stainless steel vats are increasingly popular as they are easy to cool and so offer better control over the fermentation temperature. High temperatures reduce the fruit flavours in the wine. **Maceration** is the period during which the grapes skins are left in contact with the juice. Usually lasting 5-7 days, the length of time given to maceration determines the depth of colour and tannin of the wine.

4. **Carbonic maceration** is an alternative fermentation process in which the fruit is allowed to ferment spontaneously under a protective layer of CO_2. The weight of the grapes is sufficient to crush the fruit and release the juice without mechanical pressure. These wines are soft and for drinking without ageing (e.g. Beaujolais Nouveau).

5. Pressing the grape mass (called pomace) is carried out after the 'free run' juice has been removed from the fermentation vat.

6. **Malolactic fermentation** is almost always encouraged in red winemaking. This secondary (bacterial) fermentation softens the acidity, while adding complexity and stability to the wine.

7. High quality red wines are almost always matured in oak barrels. Maturing in **oak** contributes wood tannin and vanilla flavours.

8. The wine is **racked** every few months by transferring it to a clean, sterile barrel, gently aerating it and leaving any sediment in the old barrel.

9. The wine is clarified (a process called fining) by pouring egg white or bentonite clay on to the surface.

10. A fine filter may be used to ensure stability and 'brightness' of the wine. Some winemakers believe this strips the wine of its character.

11. Because wines are susceptible to air and bacteria, the bottles are sterilised and filled in the absence of air.

Microorganisms & Biotechnology

Code: RA 2

Ageing: The wine is aged in oak barrels, where changes in the aroma and flavours occur. The extent and type of barrel ageing varies depending on wine type and quality.

Monitoring the wine: The wine is tested regularly in the barrel as it ages to check sugar and alcohol content. Here, the winemaker uses a **hydrometer** to measure the specific gravity of the wine.

Bottling: Quality control and sterile conditions during the bottling process are very important. Bottle ageing before release is still important for some red wines but is becoming less common.

1. Using the information above and on the previous page for guidance, investigate the wine making process for a named red wine. Note that in the diagram shown on the previous page, obligatory processes in the production are indicated by black arrows and white arrows indicate alternative or additional stages. Summarise the important points in the process in the spaces provided below:

(a) Name of red wine and winemaker (if relevant): _____

(b) Steps in production, including any special processes and the reasons for these: _____

_____

_____

_____

_____

_____

_____

_____

_____

_____

_____

_____

_____

_____

_____

_____

_____

_____

(c) Special features of the process for this example: _____

_____

_____

_____

_____

_____

_____

_____

Beer Brewing

Brewing is one of the oldest forms of traditional biotechnology. 5000 years ago, the ancient Sumerians and Babylonians used yeast (without knowing what it was) to brew beer, which they flavoured with cinnamon. Today, most beers are made from barley and hops. Brewing is divisible into seven stages, with finishing being an important final part of the whole process. At this stage, bacterial proteases are added to break down the yeast and prevent cloudiness. Amyloglucosidases are used to break down sugars in the production of low calorie beers. Traditional beers are stored in barrels and allowed to condition to develop their characteristic qualities. Modern beers are pasteurised, and standardised for colour and flavour before bottling.

The Commercial Production of Beer

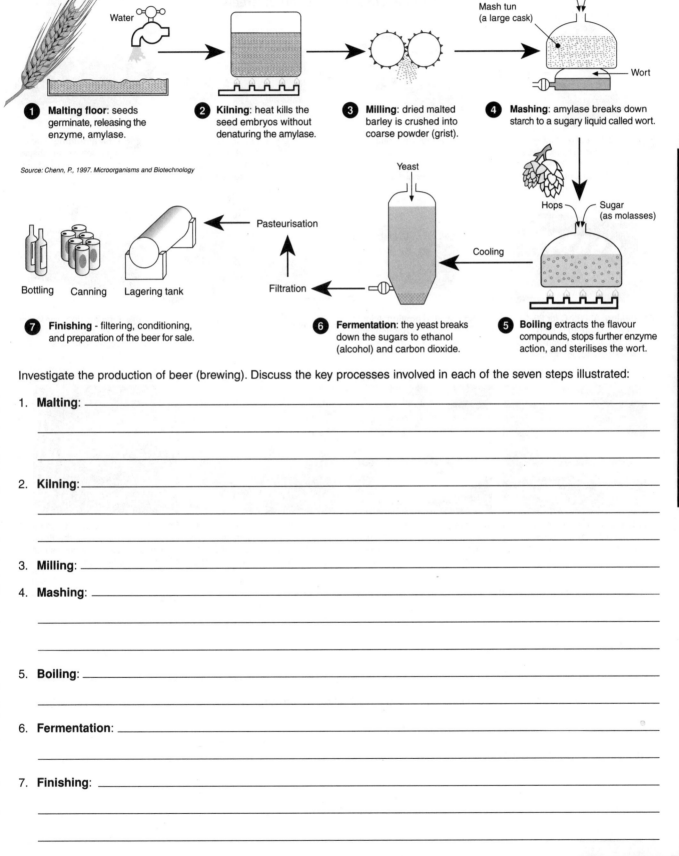

Source: Chenn, P., 1997. Microorganisms and Biotechnology

1. **Malting floor**: seeds germinate, releasing the enzyme, amylase.

2. **Kilning**: heat kills the seed embryos without denaturing the amylase.

3. **Milling**: dried malted barley is crushed into coarse powder (grist).

4. **Mashing**: amylase breaks down starch to a sugary liquid called wort.

5. **Boiling** extracts the flavour compounds, stops further enzyme action, and sterilises the wort.

6. **Fermentation**: the yeast breaks down the sugars to ethanol (alcohol) and carbon dioxide.

7. **Finishing** - filtering, conditioning, and preparation of the beer for sale.

Investigate the production of beer (brewing). Discuss the key processes involved in each of the seven steps illustrated:

1. **Malting**: _____
   _____
   _____

2. **Kilning**: _____
   _____
   _____

3. **Milling**: _____

4. **Mashing**: _____
   _____
   _____

5. **Boiling**: _____
   _____

6. **Fermentation**: _____
   _____

7. **Finishing**: _____
   _____
   _____

Microorganisms & Biotechnology

Code: RA 3

Bread Making

Using yeast to make foods and drinks is probably the oldest form of biotechnology. Modern methods of bread making use varieties of the yeast *Saccharomyces*. When the raw ingredients are mixed, the proteins in the flour (called gluten) are hydrated and they coalesce to form a sticky, elastic dough. Enzymes, having survived the milling process when grains are made into flour, act on the starch in the dough to make a mixture of sugars. During the leavening or proving process, yeast uses the sugars (anaerobically) and produces ethanol and carbon dioxide gas which causes the bread to rise. *Lactobacilli* may grow during the early stages of proving, producing lactic acid which contributes to the final flavour and inhibits growth of other organisms. Baking inactivates the yeast, evaporates the ethanol, and stops the enzymatic reactions as it cooks the flour. Bakeries may add other ingredients such as vitamin C, whiteners, raising agents, stabilisers, and flavourings.

The Commercial Production of Bread

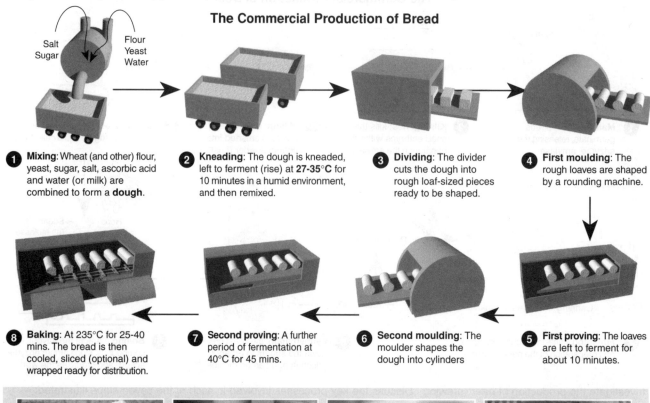

Salt
Sugar

Flour
Yeast
Water

1 **Mixing**: Wheat (and other) flour, yeast, sugar, salt, ascorbic acid and water (or milk) are combined to form a **dough**.

2 **Kneading**: The dough is kneaded, left to ferment (rise) at **27-35°C** for 10 minutes in a humid environment, and then remixed.

3 **Dividing**: The divider cuts the dough into rough loaf-sized pieces ready to be shaped.

4 **First moulding**: The rough loaves are shaped by a rounding machine.

8 **Baking**: At 235°C for 25-40 mins. The bread is then cooled, sliced (optional) and wrapped ready for distribution.

7 **Second proving**: A further period of fermentation at 40°C for 45 mins.

6 **Second moulding**: The moulder shapes the dough into cylinders

5 **First proving**: The loaves are left to ferment for about 10 minutes.

Bread making is one of the oldest and simplest of biotechnologies, involving mixing of wheat flour, water, and yeast to form a **dough**.

Kneading results in the physical and chemical changes in the gluten (flour proteins) which give the dough its elastic and resilient texture.

During **proving**, the dough is left to ferment and the yeast metabolises sugars to produce ethanol and CO_2. The CO_2 causes the dough to rise.

Baking kills the yeast, evaporates the ethanol, and cooks the flour. Modern bakeries can produce about 10 000 loaves per hour.

1. Explain the role of each of the following in the bread-making process:

   (a) Sugar: _____

   (b) Yeast: _____

   (c) Water (or milk): _____

2. (a) Explain what happens to the dough during the fermentation (or proving) stages: _____

   _____

   (b) Suggest why the dough goes through two fermentations: _____

   _____

3. Suggest why gluten free bread is flat and dense: _____

   _____

Cheese Making

Milk is composed of approximately 4% fat, 3% protein (mostly casein) and 5% lactose (milk sugar). The rest is mainly water. All cheese production requires the formation of a solid curd which, in ripened cheeses, is formed by the action of an enzyme, rennin (chymosin). Curds formed by the addition of acid are used to make fresh cheeses like cottage and cream cheese. The diagram below outlines the processes involved in creating different varieties of ripened cheeses. Most share the same basic steps.

Milk is delivered under refrigeration. Most cheese is made from cow's milk, but goat and sheep milk is used for some cheese varieties (such as feta).

Milk vats

1 The pasteurised milk is pumped into large, temperature controlled vats. The properties of the milk can vary a lot, depending on the animal's diet and whether or not the milk from the morning or evening milking is used. Small scale cheese-makers are concerned with these variations in milk quality but large Cheddar factories use so much milk that minor variations are not noticeable.

Stirring rennin and starter

2 Cheesemakers add a culture of specially selected starter bacteria (these are usually strains of *Streptoccoccus cremoris*). About 1-2 litres (containing 500 million bacteria per gram) is added to each 100 litres of milk. Rennin (milk coagulating enzyme) is also added at this point. Rennin is aided in its action by the acidic conditions produced by the bacteria. As the acidity increases, the rennin coagulates the milk proteins causing them to form a gel-like substance.

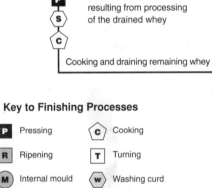

Ricotta - a low fat cheese resulting from processing of the drained whey

(P)(S)(C)

Cooking and draining remaining whey

Cutting the curd

3 Cutting the gel causes it to separate into curds (solid part) and whey (liquid part). The whey is removed from the curd by a combination of stirring, cooking, draining, salting and pressing. The vigour with which the whey is removed has a profound effect on the final cheese product.

Photo above: Appraising the final product.

All photos kindly supplied by
Kapiti Cheeses Ltd

Key to Finishing Processes

- **P** Pressing
- **R** Ripening
- **M** Internal mould
- **M** External mould
- **CH** Cheddaring*
- **C** Cooking
- **T** Turning
- **W** Washing curd
- **B** Brining**
- **S** Salting

* Cheddaring involves the 'milling' (breaking up) of cooked curd and stirring

** Brining involves soaking in a salt solution

Ripened cheeses

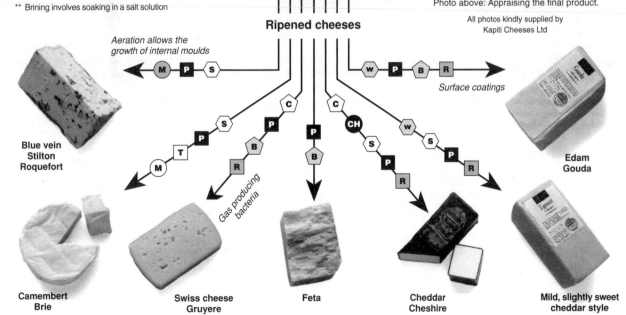

Aeration allows the growth of internal moulds

(M)(P)(S) — Blue vein / Stilton / Roquefort

(W)(P)(B)(R) Surface coatings — Edam / Gouda

Gas producing bacteria

(M)(T)(P)(S) — Camembert / Brie

(P)(B)(R) — Swiss cheese / Gruyere

(P)(B) — Feta

(C)(CH)(S)(P)(R) — Cheddar / Cheshire

(C)(W)(S)(P)(R) — Mild, slightly sweet cheddar style

In cheese making, a considerable range of starter cultures are used. For most cheeses, cultured at 30°C and 38°C, strains of *Streptococcus cremoris* are used. For cheeses requiring higher cooking temperatures (swiss and parmesan cheeses) thermophilic bacteria, which grow best at 42°C, are used (*Streptococcus thermophilus* and *Lactobacillus helveticus*). Additional microorganisms are used to give specific characteristics to cheeses. *Propionibacterium shermanii* produces the carbon dioxide gas that produces the holes in swiss cheese and creates the typical sweet nutty flavour. Blue-green moulds (*Penicillium* spp.) produce the veining on blue cheese. The texture of the cheese is loose enough that adequate oxygen can reach the aerobic moulds. Fungi contribute to these cheeses by using the lactic acids produced during the cheese making process and releasing odorous by products as a result. These give the cheeses their characteristic smells.

In making Brie and Camembert cheeses, the curds are poured into round moulds. These are then pressed and ripened (see next photograph).

The characteristic rinds of Camembert and Brie are produced by white moulds. Here a paint brush applies a coating for smear ripening the cheese.

Some cheeses are waxed while they mature. They are marketed with this coating in place. Here cheddar is being waxed by dipping into a hot tub.

All photos: Kapiti Cheeses Ltd

1. In the production of most cheese types, the bacterium *Streptococcus cremoris* is used. Explain why thermophilic bacterial varieties are used for producing cheeses requiring higher cooking temperatures:

   _____

   _____

2. Explain why the loose texture of a blue cheese is important for the development of the internal mould:

   _____

3. The texture of a cheddar is dry and somewhat crumbly. Explain how cheddaring contributes to these qualities:

   _____

   _____

4. Cheese makers take great care not to introduce foreign mould spores into the area when desirable moulds are being introduced. Explain why they are careful in this respect:

   _____

   _____

   _____

   _____

5. Using the information provided for guidance, investigate the cheese making process for a named cheese. Summarise the important points in the process in the spaces provided below. If required, develop this summary as a separate report:

   (a) Name of the cheese and cheesemaker (if relevant): _____

   (b) Microorganisms involved: _____

   (c) Steps in production, including the reasons for these (list): _____

   _____

   _____

   (d) Special features of the process for this example (list or briefly describe): _____

   _____

   _____

   _____

Yoghurt Making

The biochemistry of yoghurt production is similar to that of cheese: suitable lactic acid **bacteria** are inoculated into milk and the **lactic acid** they produce coagulates the milk proteins and thickens the yoghurt. The starter culture for yoghurt contains roughly equal amounts of two **symbiotic** bacteria, ***Lactobacillus bulgaricus*** and ***Streptococcus thermophilus***. *L. bulgaricus* metabolises lactose in the milk anaerobically to produce the lactic acid responsible for the formation of the yoghurt. *L. bulgaricus* also produces peptidases, which break down the milk proteins into peptides and amino acids. These stimulate the growth of the *Streptococcus* in the culture. *S. thermophilus* produces carbon dioxide and methanoic acid, which together lower the pH and, in turn, stimulate the growth and metabolism of the *Lactobacillus*. Natural yoghurt's characteristic flavour comes from the **lactic acid** and from **ethanal**, a metabolic by-product released by both bacteria. Traditional yoghurt was much thinner and more acidic than the commercially available yoghurt today. The addition of flavouring, colouring and fruit pulp have been developed to cater for modern tastes and recently so-called 'bio' yoghurts produce a milder tasting, sweeter, creamier yoghurt. 'Bio' yoghurts use *L. acidophilus* and *Bifidobacterium bifidum* incubated at a lower temperature for a longer period of time.

The Commercial Production of Yoghurt

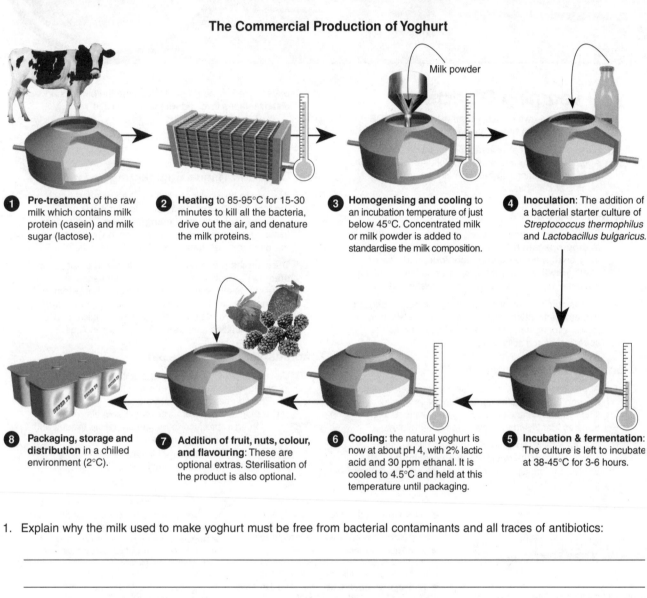

1. **Pre-treatment** of the raw milk which contains milk protein (casein) and milk sugar (lactose).

2. **Heating** to 85-95°C for 15-30 minutes to kill all the bacteria, drive out the air, and denature the milk proteins.

3. **Homogenising and cooling** to an incubation temperature of just below 45°C. Concentrated milk or milk powder is added to standardise the milk composition.

Milk powder

4. **Inoculation:** The addition of a bacterial starter culture of *Streptococcus thermophilus* and *Lactobacillus bulgaricus*.

5. **Incubation & fermentation:** The culture is left to incubate at 38-45°C for 3-6 hours.

6. **Cooling:** the natural yoghurt is now at about pH 4, with 2% lactic acid and 30 ppm ethanal. It is cooled to 4.5°C and held at this temperature until packaging.

7. **Addition of fruit, nuts, colour, and flavouring:** These are optional extras. Sterilisation of the product is also optional.

8. **Packaging, storage and distribution** in a chilled environment (2°C).

Microorganisms & Biotechnology

1. Explain why the milk used to make yoghurt must be free from bacterial contaminants and all traces of antibiotics:

_____

_____

2. Describe the mutualistic association between the two starter bacteria, *L. bulgaricus* and *S. thermophilus*:

_____

_____

_____

_____

3. Explain why the pH falls during the incubation stage: _____

4. The packed yoghurt is stored at 2-4°C which keeps the bacteria alive but inactive. Explain why it is not necessary to kill the bacteria before eating the yoghurt:

_____

Cloning and Cell Culture

Techniques and applications for cloning and cell culture

Plant tissue culture, stem cells and tissue engineering, xenotransplantation, cloning methods and issues.

Learning Objectives

☐ 1. Compile your own glossary from the **KEY WORDS** displayed in **bold type** in the learning objectives below.

☐ 2. Explain clearly what is meant by the term **clone**. Appreciate the current and potential uses of cloning technology. Distinguish between cloned organisms and cloning of cell lines.

Plant Tissue Culture *(pages 49-50)*

☐ 3. Describe the techniques used in cloning plants by **micropropagation** (tissue culture), including reference to: **growth media, aseptic technique, and use of plant growth regulators**. Discuss, in a balanced way, the benefits and drawbacks of plant tissue culture.

☐ 4. Discuss the various applications of micropropagation in modern horticulture, including as a way in which to rapidly propagate transgenics and as a way of speeding up the selection process.

Cloning in Animals *(pages 54-57)*

☐ 5. Appreciate that cloning has traditionally been achieved through **embryo splitting**. Explain the principles involved and contrast embryo splitting with nuclear transfer, identifying the advantages of the latter.

☐ 6. Outline a technique for cloning using differentiated cells, i.e. using the **nuclear transfer technique**. Explain the principles involved and identify the purpose of each step in the process. Describe the benefits and disadvantages involved with this technique.

☐ 7. Discuss, in a balanced way, the ethics of human cloning. Appreciate why the cloning of humans is such a controversial issue.

Stem Cells and Tissue Engineering *(page 51-52)*

☐ 8. Appreciate how cells are isolated and cultured to produce banks of specific cell types for medical purposes, including **tissue engineering**. Discuss how tissues engineered from cell cultures in the laboratory are used to meet human needs and demands.

☐ 9. Describe the properties of **stem cells** and **embryonic stem cells** (**ESC**) and identify the advantages of using them in transplant technologies. Discuss how **stem cell technology** meets, or could meet, human needs and demands. In your discussion, identify technical and ethical difficulties associated with the technology.

Xenotansplantation *(page 53)*

☐ 10. Discuss aspects of xenotransplantation technology including reference to any of the following:
    (a) The source of animal organs.
    (b) Transplantation from transgenic animals.
    (c) Cloning to produce immune-compatible tissues and organs in quantities to meet demand.
    (d) The use of animals bred solely for organ supply.
    (e) The risk of **zoonotic** infections.

See page 8 for additional details of these texts:

■ Chenn, P., 1997. **Microorganisms and Biotechnology** (John Murray), pp. 76-79.

■ Freeland, P., 1999. **Microbes, Medicine and Commerce** (Hodder and Stoughton), pp. 70-1, 133-4

■ Lowrie, P., *et al.*, 2000. **Microbiology and Biotechnology** (Cambridge University Press), pp. 37-39, 76.

See page 8 for details of publishers of periodicals:

STUDENT'S REFERENCE

■ **What is a Stem Cell?** Biol. Sci. Rev., 16(2) Nov. 2003, pp. 22-23. *The nature of stem cells and their therapeutic applications.*

■ **Back from the Dead** New Scientist, 9 Oct. 1999, pp. 40-43. *One case study suggests that cloning technology can save endangered species.*

■ **Fast Tissue Culture** Biol. Sci. Rev., 10(3) Jan. 1998, pp. 2-6. *Techniques for plant propagation (includes design for a tissue culture project).*

■ **Human Cloning** Biol. Sci. Rev. 11(3) Jan. 1999, pp. 7-9. *Nuclear transfer and the ethics of the issues surrounding human and livestock cloning.*

■ **Human Cloning - Why Ban it?** Biol. Sci. Rev. 11(4) March 1999, pp. 8-9. *The ethics of human cloning and the advantages to be gained from it.*

TEACHER'S REFERENCE

■ **Cloning for Medicine** Scientific American, December 1998, pp. 30-35. *The techniques and applications of cloning, including nuclear transfer.*

■ **Into the Clone Zone** New Scientist, 9 May 1998, pp. 25-30. *Where will the breakthroughs in cloning and genetic engineering lead us?*

■ **The Stem Cell Challenge** Scientific American, June 2004, pp. 60-67. *The possibility of regenerating failing body parts with new tissues derived from stem cells has provided hope, controversy and conflicting scientific claims.*

■ **Do You Believe in Miracles** New Scientist, October 2004, pp. 36-40. *British company TriStem claims that it can retro-differentiate blood cells back to a state where they have the versatility of embryonic stem cells, and so create other kinds of tissues such as neurones and heart cells.*

■ **Growth Industry** New Scientist, 15 Nov. 1997, (Inside Science). *A biotechnology supplement: fermentation technology, GE, cloning, and grafting.*

See pages 4-5 for details of how to access **Bio Links** from our web site: **www.thebiozone.com** From Bio Links, access sites under the topics:

GENERAL BIOLOGY ONLINE RESOURCES > **Online Textbooks and Lecture Notes**: • S-Cool! A level biology revision guide ... *and others*

BIOTECHNOLOGY > **Applications in Biotechnology** > **Cloning and Tissue Culture**: • Conceiving a clone • Cloning and stem cell technology • Cloning ethics • Cloning fact sheet • Howstuffworks: How cloning works • IBAC: Growing new tissue • The mammal copiers-advances in cloning • Tissue culture in the classroom ... *and others* > **Issues & Ethics in Biotechnology**: • Bioethics for beginners • New Scientist: Cloning • RDS: Understanding animal research in medicine... *and others*

Plant Tissue Culture

Plant tissue culture, or **micropropagation**, is a method used for **cloning** plants. It is used widely for the rapid multiplication of commercially important plant species with superior genotypes, as well as in the recovery programmes for endangered plant species. Plant productivity and quality may be rapidly improved, and resistance to disease, pollutants, and insects increased. Continued culture of a limited number of cloned varieties leads to a change in the genetic composition of the population (genetic variation is reduced). New genetic stock may be introduced into cloned lines periodically to prevent this reduction in genetic diversity. Micropropagation is possible because differentiated plant cells have the potential to give rise to all the cells of an adult plant. It has considerable advantages over traditional methods of plant propagation (see table below), but it is very labour intensive. In addition, the optimal conditions for growth and regeneration must be determined and plants propagated in this way may be genetically unstable or infertile, with chromosomes structurally altered or in unusual numbers. The success of tissue culture is affected by factors such as selection of **explant** material, the composition of the culturing media, plant hormone levels, lighting, and temperature.

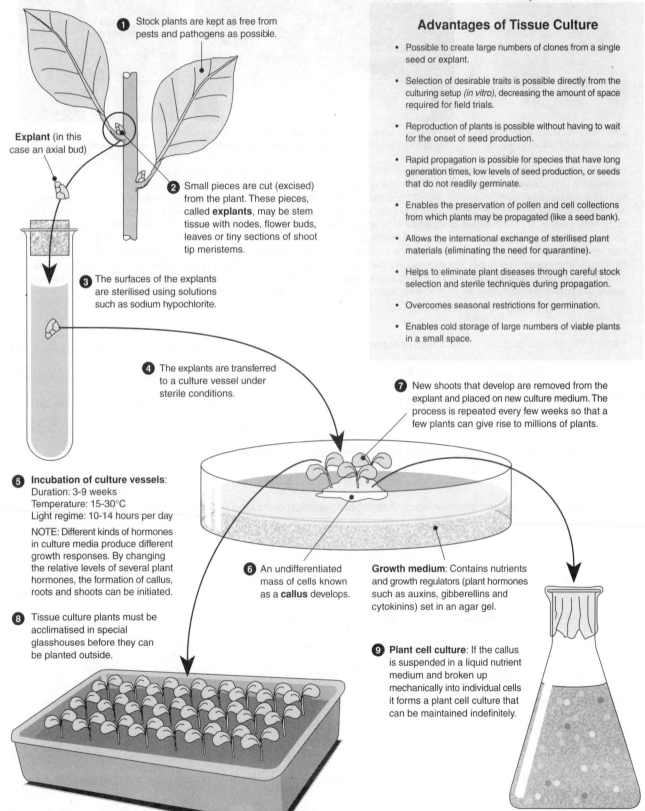

1 Stock plants are kept as free from pests and pathogens as possible.

Explant (in this case an axial bud)

2 Small pieces are cut (excised) from the plant. These pieces, called **explants**, may be stem tissue with nodes, flower buds, leaves or tiny sections of shoot tip meristems.

3 The surfaces of the explants are sterilised using solutions such as sodium hypochlorite.

4 The explants are transferred to a culture vessel under sterile conditions.

5 **Incubation of culture vessels**:
Duration: 3-9 weeks
Temperature: 15-30°C
Light regime: 10-14 hours per day

NOTE: Different kinds of hormones in culture media produce different growth responses. By changing the relative levels of several plant hormones, the formation of callus, roots and shoots can be initiated.

6 An undifferentiated mass of cells known as a **callus** develops.

7 New shoots that develop are removed from the explant and placed on new culture medium. The process is repeated every few weeks so that a few plants can give rise to millions of plants.

8 Tissue culture plants must be acclimatised in special glasshouses before they can be planted outside.

Growth medium: Contains nutrients and growth regulators (plant hormones such as auxins, gibberellins and cytokinins) set in an agar gel.

9 **Plant cell culture**: If the callus is suspended in a liquid nutrient medium and broken up mechanically into individual cells it forms a plant cell culture that can be maintained indefinitely.

Advantages of Tissue Culture

- Possible to create large numbers of clones from a single seed or explant.
- Selection of desirable traits is possible directly from the culturing setup (in vitro), decreasing the amount of space required for field trials.
- Reproduction of plants is possible without having to wait for the onset of seed production.
- Rapid propagation is possible for species that have long generation times, low levels of seed production, or seeds that do not readily germinate.
- Enables the preservation of pollen and cell collections from which plants may be propagated (like a seed bank).
- Allows the international exchange of sterilised plant materials (eliminating the need for quarantine).
- Helps to eliminate plant diseases through careful stock selection and sterile techniques during propagation.
- Overcomes seasonal restrictions for germination.
- Enables cold storage of large numbers of viable plants in a small space.

Micropropagation of the Tasmanian blackwood tree *(Acacia melanoxylon)*

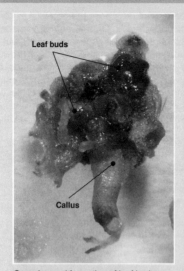
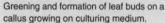

Greening and formation of leaf buds on a callus growing on culturing medium.

Normal shoots with juvenile leaves growing from a callus on media. They appear identical to those produced directly from seeds.

Seedling with juvenile foliage 6 months after transfer to greenhouse.

Micropropagation is increasingly used in conjunction with genetic engineering to propagate transgenic plants. Genetic engineering and micropropagation achieve similar results to conventional selective breeding but more precisely, quickly, and independently of growing season. The **Tasmanian blackwood** (above) is well suited to this type of manipulation. It is a versatile hardwood tree now being extensively trialled in some countries as a replacement for tropical hardwoods. The timber is of high quality, but genetic variations between individual trees lead to differences in timber quality and colour Tissue culture allows the multiple propagation of trees with desirable traits (e.g. uniform timber colour). Tissue culture could also help to find solutions to problems that cannot be easily solved by forestry management. When combined with genetic engineering (introduction of new genes into the plant) problems of pest and herbicide susceptibility may be resolved. Genetic engineering may also be used to introduce a gene for male sterility, thereby stopping pollen production. This would improve the efficiency of conventional breeding programmes by preventing self-pollination of flowers (the manual removal of stamens is difficult and very labour intensive).

Information courtesy of Raewyn Poole, University of Waikato (Unpublished Msc. thesis).

1. Explain the general purpose of plant **micropropagation** _____

   _____

2. (a) Explain what a **callus** is: _____

   _____

   (b) Explain how a callus may be stimulated to initiate root and shoot formation: _____

   _____

3. Discuss the advantages and disadvantages of **micropropagation** compared with traditional propagation methods:

   _____

   _____

   _____

   _____

   _____

   _____

   _____

   _____

   _____

4. Describe a potential problem with micropropagation in terms of long term ability to adapt to environmental changes:

   _____

   _____

Stem Cells and Tissue Engineering

Cell cultures have been used for many years for medical and research purposes, e.g. for the culture of viruses for vaccine production and in the production of monoclonal antibodies. Reliable techniques in cell culturing have paved the way for new technologies such as **cell replacement therapy** and **tissue engineering**. These technologies require a disease-free and plentiful supply of cells of specific types. Tissue engineering, for example, involves inducing living cells to grow on a scaffold of natural or synthetic material to produce a three-dimensional tissue such as bone or skin. In 1998, an artificial skin called Apligraf became the first product of this type to be approved for use as a biomedical device. It is now widely used in place of skin grafts. The applications of tissue engineering range from blood vessel replacement and skin, bone, tendon, and cartilage repair, to the treatment of degenerative nerve diseases. A key to the future of this technology will be the developments in **stem cell** research. Stem cells have the ability to develop and form all the tissues of the body. The best source of these is from very early embryos, but some adult tissues (e.g. bone marrow) also contain stem cells. Therapeutic **stem cell cloning** is still in its very early stages and, despite its enormous medical potential, research with human embryonic cells is still banned in some countries.

Engineering a Living Skin

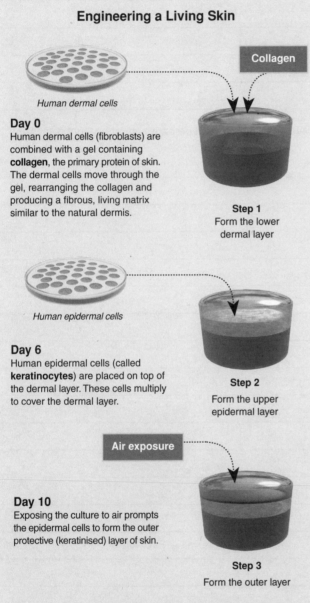

Human dermal cells

Collagen

Day 0
Human dermal cells (fibroblasts) are combined with a gel containing **collagen**, the primary protein of skin. The dermal cells move through the gel, rearranging the collagen and producing a fibrous, living matrix similar to the natural dermis.

Step 1
Form the lower dermal layer

Human epidermal cells

Day 6
Human epidermal cells (called **keratinocytes**) are placed on top of the dermal layer. These cells multiply to cover the dermal layer.

Step 2
Form the upper epidermal layer

Air exposure

Day 10
Exposing the culture to air prompts the epidermal cells to form the outer protective (keratinised) layer of skin.

Step 3
Form the outer layer

Apligraf, produced by the company Organogenesis, was the first living, tissue-engineered skin product to be commercially available. It is used to treat diabetic ulcers and burns, with the patient's own cells and tissues helping to complete the biological repair. Producing Apligraf is a three stage process (above), which results in a bilayered, living structure capable of stimulating wound repair through its own growth factors and proteins. The final size of the Apligraf product is about 75 mm and, from this, tens of thousands of pieces can be made. The cells used to start the culture are usually obtained from discarded neonatal foreskins collected after circumcision.

The Future? Embryonic Stem Cell Cloning

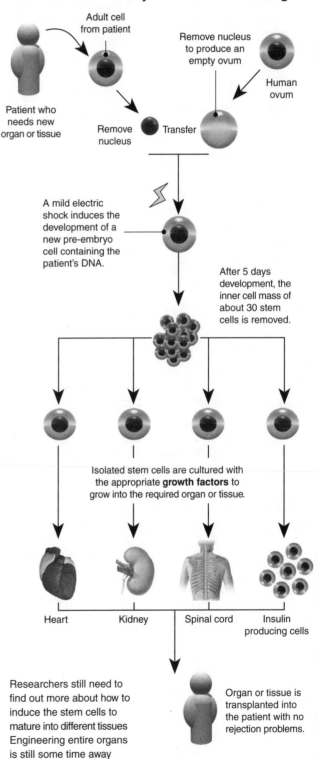

Adult cell from patient

Remove nucleus to produce an empty ovum

Human ovum

Patient who needs new organ or tissue

Remove nucleus

Transfer

A mild electric shock induces the development of a new pre-embryo cell containing the patient's DNA.

After 5 days development, the inner cell mass of about 30 stem cells is removed.

Isolated stem cells are cultured with the appropriate **growth factors** to grow into the required organ or tissue.

Heart

Kidney

Spinal cord

Insulin producing cells

Researchers still need to find out more about how to induce the stem cells to mature into different tissues Engineering entire organs is still some time away

Organ or tissue is transplanted into the patient with no rejection problems.

Cloning and Cell Culture

Code: RA 3

1. Outline the benefits of using a tissue engineered skin product, such as Apligraf, to treat wounds that require grafts:

_____

_____

2. Describe one potential advantage of embryonic stem cell cloning for tissue engineering technology:

_____

_____

3. Discuss the present and potential medical applications of tissue engineering: _____

_____

_____

_____

_____

4. Investigate the techniques or the applications of therapeutic stem cell cloning and prepare a short account discussing the technical or ethical issues involved.

_____

_____

_____

_____

_____

_____

_____

_____

_____

_____

_____

_____

_____

_____

_____

_____

_____

_____

_____

_____

_____

_____

_____

Xenotransplantation

Xenotransplantation is the transplantation of cells, tissues, or organs from one species to another. The increasing demand for human organs for clinical transplantation far exceeds the supply and xenotransplantation is a potential solution to this shortage. The use of xenotransplantation raises many challenging medical, legal, and ethical issues. These include issues of safety and procedural efficacy, as well as the necessary considerations of animal welfare. Previous attempts to carry out transplants of organs from other species into humans have been largely unsuccessful because of immuno-compatibility problems and organ rejection. Recent scientific developments in the area of genetic modification may enable some of these problems to be overcome. There are hopes that genetically modified pigs may be used to produce immuno-compatible organs for transplantation. Other procedures aim to use cells or tissues from other species to treat diabetes, cancer, liver failure, and Parkinson's disease.

Xenotransplantation

1963	Chimpanzee kidneys were transplanted into 13 patients at Tulane University, Louisianna. One patient survived 9 months.
1964	First cardiac transplant attempted to put the heart of a chimpanzee into a human.
1984	Baby Fae, born with a malformed heart, received a heart from a baboon, and lived only 20 more days.
1992	Liver transplants from baboons to humans, with one patient surviving more than two months. The massive immunosuppression necessary to avoid rejection eventually resulted in a fatal infection.
1995	Jeff Getty received immune cells from a baboon in an attempt to combat his severe AIDS. His condition mysteriously appeared to improve.
1997	Clinical trial using foetal pig nerve cells in patients with Parkinson's disease indicated some success.

Chimpanzee

Baboon

Pig

Xenotransplantation is an attempt to overcome the shortage of human donor organs by using equivalent organs from other mammals, such as baboons, chimpanzees, and pigs (pig heart valves are in common use). It has not been widely adopted or successful. There is a considerable ethical debate surrounding its use and some justified concern over the possibility of accidentally introducing new diseases into the human population. Known as **zoonoses**, such cross-species infections by viruses have already been observed (e.g. HIV and SARS).

1. (a) Describe the development of xenotransplantation in response to the shortage of donor tissues and organs:

_____

_____

_____

_____

(b) Describe the greatest challenge for xenotransplantation which has meant it has not been as successful as hoped:

_____

_____

(c) Explain why disease transmission (**xenozoonosis**) is a cause for concern: _____

_____

_____

_____

2. In point form, outline the ethical issues associated with xenotransplantation. Consider costs, benefits, source of tissue, and criteria for choosing recipients. If required, debate the issue, or develop your arguments as a separate report:

_____

_____

_____

_____

_____

_____

Code: RA 2

Cloning by Embryo Splitting

Livestock breeds frequently produce only one individual per pregnancy and all individuals in a herd will have different traits. Cloning (by embryo splitting or other means) makes it possible to produce high value herds with identical traits more quickly. This technique also has applications in the medical field, for example, in the cloning of embryonic stem cells. Such applications demonstrate the advances made recently in cloning technology. Some of the most ambitious medical projects now being considered involve the production of universal human donor cells. Scientists know how to isolate undifferentiated stem cells from early embryos in mice. They are also learning how to force stem cells to differentiate into different tissues. Such techniques may make it possible to manufacture cells or replace tissues damaged by illness (e.g. muscular dystrophy or diabetes). Individually matched stem cells could be made by transferring the nucleus from one of the patient's cells into a human egg to create an embryo. The embryo would be allowed to develop only to a stage where stem cells could be separated and cultured from it. Although the embryo would consist of only a few hundred cells, there would be many ethical issues raised by this technique.

Livestock are selected for cloning on the basis of desirable qualities such as wool, meat, or milk productivity

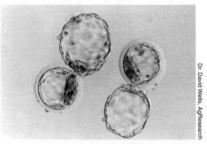

Cloned embryos immediately prior to implantation into a surrogate. These are at the blastocyst stage (a mass of cells that have begun to differentiate).

The individuals produced by embryo splitting have the same characteristics as the parents

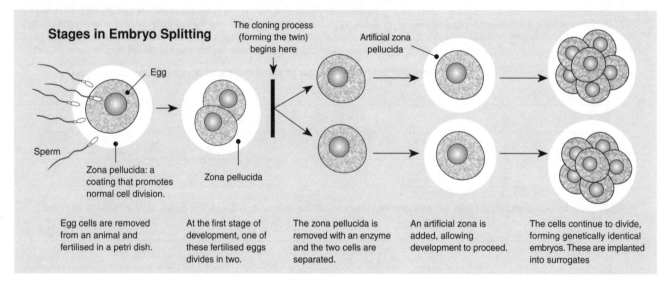

Stages in Embryo Splitting

The cloning process (forming the twin) begins here

Artificial zona pellucida

Egg

Sperm

Zona pellucida: a coating that promotes normal cell division.

Zona pellucida

Egg cells are removed from an animal and fertilised in a petri dish.

At the first stage of development, one of these fertilised eggs divides in two.

The zona pellucida is removed with an enzyme and the two cells are separated.

An artificial zona is added, allowing development to proceed.

The cells continue to divide, forming genetically identical embryos. These are implanted into surrogates

1. With respect to animals, explain the term **cloning** _____

_____

2. Briefly list the possible benefits to be gained from cloning the following:

   (a) Stem cells for medical use: _____

   _____

   _____

   _____

   (b) High milk yielding cows: _____

   _____

   _____

   _____

3. Suggest one reason why it would undesirable to produce all livestock using embryo splitting: _____

_____

Cloning by Nuclear Transfer

Clones are genetically identical individuals produced from one parent. Cloning is not new; it has been used in plant breeding for years. In recent years clones have been produced from both embryonic and non-embryonic cells using standard **nuclear transfer techniques** (below). In 2004, Australian genetic researchers successfully cloned a cow (called Brandy) using **serial nuclear transfer** (SNT) which involves an extra round of nuclear transfer to improve the reprogramming of the fused donor cells. In animal reproductive technology, cloning has facilitated the rapid production of genetically superior stock. These animals may then be dispersed among commercial herds. The **primary focus** of the new cloning technologies is to provide an economically viable way to rapidly produce transgenic animals with very precise genetic modifications.

Creating Dolly Using Standard Nuclear Transfer

Dolly, the Finn Dorset lamb born at the Roslin Institute (near Edinburgh) in July 1996, was the first mammal to be cloned from **non-embryonic cells**. Nuclear transfer has been used successfully to clone cells from embryonic tissue, but Dolly was created from a fully differentiated udder cell from a six year old ewe. This cell was made quiescent and then 'tricked' into re-entering an embryonic state. Dolly's birth was a breakthrough, because it showed that the processes leading to cell specialisation are not irreversible; even specialised cells can be 'reprogrammed' into an embryonic state. The steps involved in creating Dolly are outlined below. While cloning seems relatively easy to achieve using this method, Dolly's early death (right) has raised concerns that the techniques could have caused premature ageing. Although there is, as yet, no evidence for this, the long term viability of animals cloned from non-embryonic cells has still to be established.

Dolly Dies

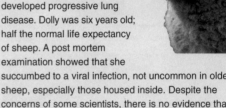
PHOTO: Courtesy Roslin Institute ©

Dolly the sheep was euthanased on **February 14th, 2003** after examinations showed she had developed progressive lung disease. Dolly was six years old; half the normal life expectancy of sheep. A post mortem examination showed that she succumbed to a viral infection, not uncommon in older sheep, especially those housed inside. Despite the concerns of some scientists, there is no evidence that cloning was a factor in Dolly contracting the disease.

1 **Donor cells taken from udder:** Cells from the udder of a Finn Dorset ewe were cultured in low nutrient medium for a week. The nutrient deprived cells stopped dividing, switched off their active genes, and became dormant.

2 **Unfertilised egg has nucleus removed:** In preparation for the nuclear transfer, an **unfertilised** egg cell was taken from a Scottish blackface ewe. Using micromanipulation techniques, the nucleus containing the DNA, was removed. This left a recipient egg cell with no nucleus, but an intact cytoplasm and the cellular machinery for producing an embryo.

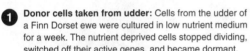
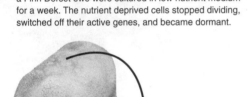

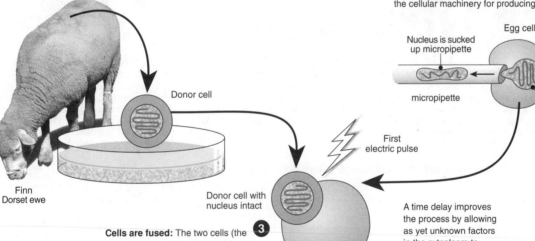

Nucleus is sucked up micropipette

Egg cell

Blunt "holding pipette"

micropipette

Nucleus of egg cell

Donor cell

First electric pulse

Finn Dorset ewe

Donor cell with nucleus intact

A time delay improves the process by allowing as yet unknown factors in the cytoplasm to activate the chromatin.

Second electric pulse

Fused cells

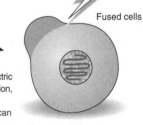

3 **Cells are fused:** The two cells (the dormant donor cell and the recipient egg cell) were placed next to each other and a gentle electric pulse causes them to fuse together (like soap bubbles).

Egg cell without nucleus

4 **Cell division is triggered:** A second electric pulse triggers cellular activity and cell division, effectively jump-starting the cell into production of an embryo. This reaction can also be triggered by chemical means.

PHOTO: Courtesy Roslin Institute ©

Blackface ewe

Dolly

5 After six days, the resulting embryo was surgically implanted into the uterus of the surrogate mother; another Scottish blackface ewe. Of the hundreds of reconstructed eggs, only 29 successfully formed embryos, and only Dolly survived to birth.

6 **Birth:** After a gestation of 148 days, the pregnant blackface ewe gave birth to Dolly, the Finn Dorset lamb that is genetically identical to the original donor

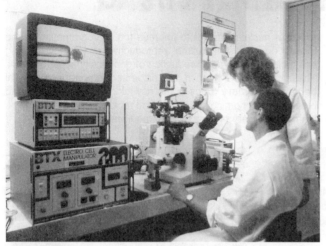

Dr David Wells and Pavla Misica in the embryo micromanipulation laboratory at AgResearch in Hamilton, New Zealand (monitor's image is enlarged on the right).

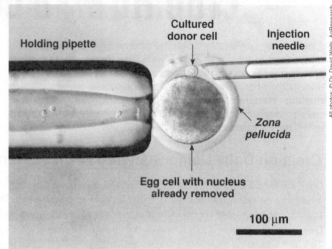

A single cultured cell is injected underneath the *zona pellucida* (the outer membrane) and positioned next to the egg cell (step 3 of diagram on the left).

Adult cloning heralds a new chapter in the breeding of livestock. Traditional breeding methods are slow, unpredictable, and suffer from a time delay in waiting to see what the phenotype is like before breeding the next generation. Adult cloning methods now allow a rapid spread of valuable livestock into commercial use among farmers. It will also allow the livestock industry to respond rapidly to market changes in the demand for certain traits in livestock products. In New Zealand, 10 healthy clones were produced from a single cow (the differences in coat colour patterns arise from the random migration of pigment cells in early embryonic development).

Lady is the last surviving cow of the rare Enderby Island (south of N.Z.) cattle breed. Adult cloning was used to produce her genetic duplicate, Elsie (born 31 July 1998). This result represents the first demonstration of the use of adult cloning in animal conservation.

1. Explain how cloning using **nuclear transfer** techniques differs from **embryo splitting**:

   _____

   _____

   _____

   _____

2. Explain how each of the following events is controlled in the **nuclear transfer** process:

   (a) The switching off of all genes in the donor cell: _____

   _____

   (b) The fusion (combining) of donor cell with enucleated egg cell: _____

   _____

   (c) The activation of the cloned cell into producing an embryo: _____

   _____

3. Describe a potential application of nuclear transfer technology for the cloning of animals: _____

   _____

   _____

The Human Cloning Debate

The most controversial aspect of cloning is the potential to clone humans. In situations where couples cannot have children or where one prospective parent has a heritable genetic disease, cloning could produce a healthy child that is genetically the couple's own. However, the issue of human cloning raises concerns that clones may be generated out of vanity or that couples may want 'designer' clones, e.g. of celebrities. One of the most promising applications of cloning is in the production of **stem cells**. Stem cells have the ability to generate a variety of cell types. This makes them potentially very useful for the treatment of a number of diseases. In many cases of traditional tissue transplantation, the patient's immune system rejects the donated cells. Cloning could solve this problem; if a patient's own cells could be used to generate stem cells, there would be no risk of rejection. Similarly, cloned stem cells could generate organs for transplantation. This would prevent immune rejection problems and alleviate the problem of organ shortages. Despite the potential benefits of cloning, there are enormous moral and ethical concerns surrounding its use. Before cloning can become a viable technology, these concerns need to be addressed.

Arguments Used **Against** Human Cloning	Arguments Used **For** Human Cloning
• Cloning might lead to the creation of genetically engineered groups of people for specific purposes, such as for warfare or slavery. • Cloning might lead to an attempt to improve the human race according to an arbitrary standard. • Cloning could result in the introduction of additional defects in the human gene pool. • Cloning is unsafe. There are too many unknown factors that could adversely affect the offspring. • A clone may have a diminished sense of individuality. • A clone may have fewer rights than other people. • Clones may be created with the sole intention of using them as a source of organs and tissues for transplantation. • Cloning is at odds with the traditional concept of family. • Cloning is against God's will. • Some aspects of human life should be off limits to science. • The cloning technique has not been perfected. Scientists expect that any attempt to clone a human would, as in the work that led to Dolly, result in the death of many embryos and newborns before success was achieved.	• Cloning would enable infertile couples to have children of their own. • Cloning would give couples at risk of producing a child with a genetic defect the chance to produce a healthy child. • Cloning could shed light on how genes work and could lead to the discovery of new treatments for genetic diseases. • A ban on cloning may be unconstitutional. It would deprive people of the right to reproduce and restrict scientific freedom. • A clone would not really be a duplicate, because environmental factors would mould him or her into a unique individual. • A clone would have as much of a sense of individuality as do twins. • A clone would have the same rights as do all other people. • Cloning is comparable in safety to a number of other medical procedures. • The current objections to cloning are similar to objections raised against scientific procedures developed earlier that are now largely accepted. Examples include heart transplants and some of the standard reproductive technologies (IVF).

Source: www.worldbook.com

1. Conduct a **survey** of your class, or perhaps even a wider sample of part of your school, to determine whether people approve or disapprove of the cloning of human embryos for the following purposes. Convert your results into percentages approving or disapproving of the use and enter them in the spaces below:

   (a) To provide infertile couples using test tube *in vitro* fertilization with more embryos to increase their chances of conceiving.

   Approve: _____ Disapprove: _____

   (b) To make it easier for scientists to screen embryos for inherited abnormalities (such as cystic fibrosis and Huntington disease).

   Approve: _____ Disapprove: _____

   (c) To produce babies whose vital organs can be used to save the life of others, such as a sibling requiring a bone marrow transplant.

   Approve: _____ Disapprove: _____

   (d) To make it possible for parents to have a twin at a later date.

   Approve: _____ Disapprove: _____

   (e) To establish 'embryo banks' from which prospective parents could select a child with genetic desirable traits.

   Approve: _____ Disapprove: _____

   (f) To make it possible for societies to clone and reproduce a number of individuals with genetically desirable traits for specific purposes (e.g. academics, soldiers, basketball players, or musicians).

   Approve: _____ Disapprove: _____

   (g) Your 2 month old baby is about to be taken off life support. You and your partner can no longer conceive children. Would you clone the child if it were an option?

   Approve: _____ Disapprove: _____

   (h) Do you consider rejecting an 8-cell embryo produced in a lab to be an abortion?

   Yes: _____ No: _____

   (i) If scientist were able to produce new organs using your cells and cloning technology, would you consider receiving them.

   Yes: _____ No: _____

   (Source: questions (a) - (f) CNN/TIME Magazine survey, 8 Nov 1993, p53)

Cloning and Cell Culture

Code: A 2

Genetic Manipulation

Techniques and applications in genetic engineering

DNA ligation, restriction enzymes, gel electrophoresis, PCR, gene cloning, and transgenesis. Ethics of GMO technology.

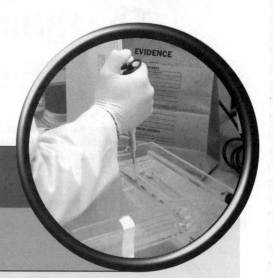

Learning Objectives

☐ 1. Compile your own glossary from the **KEY WORDS** displayed in **bold type** in the learning objectives below.

Introduction to Gene Technology *(page 60)*

☐ 2. Explain what is meant by **gene technology** and distinguish it from the more general term, **biotechnology**. Distinguish between **genetic engineering** and **genetic modification** in general. Recognise one as a subset of the other.

☐ 3. Recognise that a small number of basic techniques (restriction digestion, DNA ligation, gel electrophoresis, and PCR) are used in a number of different processes (e.g. gene cloning, transgenesis, DNA profiling). Appreciate that these processes have wide application.

☐ 4. Provide an outline of the various applications of gene technology in modern medicine, agriculture, and industry. Appreciate the pivotal role of microorganisms in the development and application of this technology.

Techniques in Gene Technology

Restriction enzymes and ligation *(pages 61-63)*

☐ 5. Explain the terms **restriction enzyme**, **plasmid**, and **recognition site**. Describe the basis by which restriction enzymes work, distinguishing between **sticky end** and **blunt end** DNA fragments produced by different types of restriction enzymes.

☐ 6. Identify the role of restriction enzymes in **recombinant DNA technology**. Identify some commonly used restriction enzymes and their sources, and give their recognition sites.

☐ 7. Explain what is meant by **DNA ligation**. Describe the purpose of ligation and how it is achieved. Explain the role of **DNA ligase** in the technique.

☐ 8. Explain what is meant by **annealing**. Describe how **recombinant DNA** is produced by the ligation of DNA from different sources.

Gel electrophoresis of DNA *(page 64)*

☐ 9. Explain the role of **gel electrophoresis** (of DNA) in gene technology (also see #27). Outline the major steps in the technique, including the role of **restriction digestion**. Name an example of a gel commonly used in gel electrophoresis and identify the properties of the gel that facilitate the separation of DNA fragments.

☐ 10. Explain how the DNA fragments on a gel are made visible. Describe the role of **DNA markers** in identifying fragments of different size.

Polymerase chain reaction *(pages 65-66)*

☐ 11. Explain the role of **polymerase chain reaction** (PCR) in **DNA amplification**. Explain why PCR is an essential tool for many procedures in gene technology.

☐ 12. Describe the basic technique of PCR, including the role of **primers**, **nucleotides**, and **DNA polymerase**.

Processes & Applications in Gene Technology

Gene cloning *(pages 67-68)*

☐ 13. Explain what is meant by **gene cloning** and describe applications of this technology. Recognise the stages involved in gene cloning: preparation of the clone (isolation of the gene and its insertion into a vector) and the actual cloning of the gene itself (achieved through rapid multiplication of the microbial host cell).

☐ 14. Outline the steps in preparing a gene for cloning:
   • Explain how the desired gene is **isolated** from cells.
   • Outline the role of **reverse transcriptase** in creating the gene for insertion into the plasmid vector.
   • Explain the role of **restriction enzymes** and **DNA ligation** in inserting the gene into an appropriate vector (e.g. plasmid) to create a **molecular clone**.

☐ 15. Outline how the prepared molecular clone (containing the desired gene) is introduced into the host cells. Describe how bacterial colonies with the desired gene are identified (e.g. with **marker genes**) and isolated. Understand that these bacteria are then grown in culture to produce multiple copies of the gene.

☐ 16. Explain how gene expression is achieved in the organism that receives the molecular clone, e.g. in a crop plant where a gene of interest is introduced using the bacterium *Agrobacterium tumefaciens*.

Transgenic organisms *(pages 69-70)*

☐ 17. Explain clearly what is meant by a **transgenic organism**. Note the use of the term **transformation**, which is used specifically for the acquisition of genetic material by the uptake of **naked DNA** by the recipient. Transformation is a term most often used with respect to bacteria (in which transformation occurs naturally), but increasingly applied to other organisms.

☐ 18. Describe the techniques involved in producing transgenic organisms, including the role of viral or **plasmid vectors** in integrating foreign DNA into the genome of another organism. Understand that organisms are usually transformed with **recombinant vectors** produced using **restriction enzymes** and **DNA ligation**.

☐ 19. Explain the role of **marker genes** (also called genetic markers) in identifying transformed cells.

Meeting Human Demands *(pages 60, 71-73, 77-87)*

☐ 20. Describe the production of **chymosin** (rennin) from genetically modified (GM) microbes (yeast or bacteria) and describe its use in the dairy industry. Discuss any benefits and disadvantages of using enzymes, such as chymosin, from a GM source, and compare these with the benefits and disadvantages of traditional methods.

☐ 21. Discuss the potential of genetically modified organisms (GMOs) to meet human needs: Consider:

(a) Crop resistance to herbicides and/or insect pests.

(b) Expansion of crop growing range (changes in environmental tolerance).

(c) Improved storage and/or improvement of crop quality (e.g. amino acid composition, protein content, or yield of useable plant).

☐ 22. Recognise and discuss the use of genetic engineering techniques in meeting human needs and demands in other areas such as the medical and pharmaceutical industries (e.g. the production of new drugs and vaccines, gene therapy, use of transgenic livestock to produce pharmaceuticals).

Ethics of Gene Technology *(pages 74-75)*

Discuss (in a balanced way) the relevant ethical, social, and economic issues associated with the use of genetically engineered organisms. You could consider all or some of:

☐ 23. Discuss the real and perceived risks associated with transgenic organisms. Contrast these risks for GM plants and animals. Recognise and discuss the advantages and disadvantages of using transgenic organisms in agriculture and industry.

☐ 24. Demonstrate an understanding of the social and moral implications of gene technology. These apply particularly to *gene therapy, genetic screening, non-therapeutic genetic manipulation,* and *animal welfare.*

☐ 25. Consider the economic issues associated with the use of gene technology. Examples include: the impact of **patents** for GMOs and consequent control over a product (e.g. seeds), insurance against GMO problems/accidents, and the cost of staying GM-free.

Review of Techniques & Applications in Biotechnology *(see Appendix)*

☐ 26. Review and summarise the techniques used in the following applications in gene technology: gene cloning, transgenesis, DNA profiling, genome analysis, stem cell research, and xenotransplantation.

See page 8 for additional details of these texts:

■ Chenn, P., 1997. **Microorganisms and Biotechnology** (John Murray), chpt 5.

■ Clegg, C.J., 2002. **Microbes in Action** (John Murray), chpt 8.

■ Freeland, P., 1999. **Microbes, Medicine and Commerce** (Hodder and Stoughton), chpt 3, 6, & 8.

■ Jones, N., *et al.,* 2001. **The Essentials of Genetics** (John Murray), chpt 18.

■ Lowrie, P., *et al.,* 2000. **Microbiology and Biotechnology** (Cambridge University Press), chpt 4.

■ Taylor, J., 2001. **Microorganisms and Biotechnology** (NelsonThornes), pp. 115-116.

See page 8 for details of publishers of periodicals:

STUDENT'S REFERENCE

■ **Special Report: Living in a GM World** New Scientist, 31 October 1998 (whole issue). *Nine feature articles on GMOs: uses, risks, and benefits.*

■ **The Polymerase Chain Reaction** Biol. Sci. Rev., 16(3) Feb. 2004, pp. 10-13. *This account explains the techniques and applications of PCR.*

■ **Agro-Biotech** Biol. Sci. Rev., 16(1) Sept. 2003, pp. 21-24. *Genetic engineering provides a tool to improving crops and meeting consumer demand. What is being developed and what are the risks?*

Presentation MEDIA
to support this topic:

Genetics & Evolution CD-ROM:
• **Set 9: Gene Technology**

■ **Birds, Bees, and Superweeds** Biol. Sci. Rev., 17(2) Nov. 2004, pp. 24-27. *Genetically modified crops: their advantages and commercial applications, as well as some of the risks and concerns associated with their use.*

■ **Genetically Engineered Bacteria** Biol. Sci. Rev., 10(1) Sept. 1997, pp. 2-6. *Genetic engineering of bacteria for use in industry and the use of plasmids as vectors for transformation.*

■ **Food for All** New Scientist, 31 October 1998, pp. 50-52. *Crops that resist drought and disease could transform the lives of the poor. What problems are inherent in the dissemination of GM crops?*

■ **Food / How Altered?** National Geographic, May 2002, pp. 32-50. *An account of the issue of "biotech foods". What are they, how altered are they, and how safe are they?*

■ **GM Food Safety Special Report** Scientific American, April 2001. *Special issue examining aspects of the GM food debate (excellent).*

■ **Genetically Modified Plants** Biol. Sci. Rev., 12(3) January 2000, pp. 2-7. *The creation of GM foods and their benefits and risks to the consumer.*

■ **Genetic Manipulation of Plants** Biol. Sci. Rev., 15(1) Sept. 2002, pp. 10-13. *The aims, methods, and applications of plant genetic engineering.*

■ **Genetics and Ecology** Biol. Sci. Rev., 16(3) Feb. 2004, pp. 14-17. *Genetic profiling of threatened species can be used in population management providing knowledge of population size, migration, and genetic diversity.*

■ **Live and Let Live** New Scientist, 31 Oct. 1998, pp. 46-49. *Scientific and ethical arguments for and against genetically engineered crops.*

■ **GM Food Safety Special Report** Scientific American, April 2001. *Special issue examining aspects of the GM food debate (excellent).*

TEACHER'S REFERENCE

■ **Back to the Future of Cereals** Scientific American, August 2004, pp. 26-33. *An excellent, up-to-date account of the state of crop technology. Fuelled by genomic studies, a new green revolution is predicted to increase crop yields even further.*

■ **Making Rice Disease Resistant** Scientific American, November 1997, pp. 68-73. *Genetic engineering of rice will protect this major crop from disease. Covers both technique and application.*

■ **Begone! Evil Genes** New Scientist, 6 July 2002, pp. 32-37. *A new "exorcist" technology addresses many of the concerns people have about growing crops from GM seeds.*

See pages 4-5 for details of how to access **Bio Links** from our web site: **www.thebiozone.com** From Bio Links, access sites under the topics:

> **Online Textbooks and Lecture Notes**: • An on-line biology book • Biology-online Org *... and others* > **General Online Biology Resources**: • Access excellence *... and others* > **Glossaries**: • Applied biology glossary • Biotechnology and food glossary • Genome glossary • Glossary of molecular biology terms

BIOTECHNOLOGY: > **General Biotechnology Sites**: • Molecular genetics *... and others* > **Biotechnology Techniques** • Gel electrophoresis slide presentation • Interactive biotechnology • Molecular techniques • Restriction enzymes • Principle of the PCR • Recombinant DNA *... and others* > **Biotechnology Processes**: • Animal and plant transformation • Basics of DNA fingerprinting • DNA fingerprinting in human health and society • DNA fingerprinting via Southern blotting • DNA workshop • Transgenic organisms *... and others* > **Applications in Biotechnology**: > **Food Biotechnology - GM Foods**: A GM world • Food biotechnology • Food for our future *... and others* > **Industrial Biotechnology**: • Biotechnology in industry • Discover biotech *... and others* > **Issues & Ethics in Biotechnology**: • Bioethics for beginners • Ethical, legal, and social issues-HGP • Genetic engineering and its dangers *... and others* > **DNA Software Download**: • Chromas DNA sequence viewer *... and others*

The Nature of GMOs

The genetic modification of organisms is a vast industry, and the applications of the technology are exciting and far reaching. It brings new hope for medical cures, promises to increase yields in agriculture, and has the potential to help solve the world's pollution and resource crises. Organisms with artificially altered DNA are referred to as **genetically modified organisms** or **GMOs**. They may be modified in one of three ways (outlined below). Some of the current and proposed applications of gene technology raise complex ethical and safety issues, where the benefits of their use must be carefully weighed against the risks to human health, as well as the health and well-being of other organisms and the environment as a whole.

Producing Genetically Modified Organisms (GMOs)

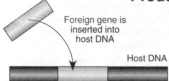
Foreign gene is inserted into host DNA — Host DNA

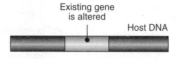
Existing gene is altered — Host DNA

Gene is deleted or deactivated — Host DNA

Add a foreign gene

A novel (foreign) gene is inserted from another species. This will enable the GMO to express the trait coded by the new gene. Organisms genetically altered in this way are referred to as **transgenic**.

Alter an existing gene

An existing gene may be altered to make it express at a higher level (e.g. growth hormone) or in a different way (in tissue that would not normally express it). This method is also used for gene therapy.

Delete or 'turn off' a gene

An existing gene may be deleted or deactivated to prevent the expression of a trait (e.g. the deactivation of the ripening gene in tomatoes).

Applications of GMOs

Extending shelf life
Some fresh produce (e.g. tomatoes) have been engineered to have an extended keeping quality. In the case of tomatoes, the gene for ripening has been switched off, delaying the natural process of softening in the fruit.

Pest or herbicide resistance
Plants can be engineered to produce their own insecticide and become pest resistant. Genetically engineered herbicide resistance is also common. In this case, chemical weed killers can be used freely without crop damage.

Crop improvement
Gene technology is now an integral part of the development of new crop varieties. Crops can be engineered to produce higher protein levels or to grow in inhospitable conditions (e.g. salty or arid conditions).

Environmental clean-up
Some bacteria have been engineered to thrive on waste products, such as liquefied newspaper pulp or oil. As well as degrading pollutants and wastes, the bacteria may be harvested as a commercial protein source.

Biofactories
Transgenic bacteria are widely used to produce desirable products: often hormones or proteins. Large quantities of a product can be produced using bioreactors (above). Examples: insulin production by recombinant yeast, production of bovine growth hormone.

Vaccine development
The potential exists for multipurpose vaccines to be made using gene technology. Genes coding for vaccine components (e.g. viral protein coat) are inserted into an unrelated live vaccine (e.g. polio vaccine), and deliver proteins to stimulate an immune response.

Livestock improvement using transgenic animals
Transgenic sheep have been used to enhance wool production in flocks (above, left). The keratin protein of wool is largely made of a single amino acid, cysteine. Injecting developing sheep with the genes for the enzymes that generate cysteine produces woollier transgenic sheep. In some cases, transgenic animals have been used as biofactories. Transgenic sheep carrying the human gene for a protein, α-1-antitrypsin produce the protein in their milk. The antitrypsin is extracted from the milk and used to treat hereditary emphysema.

1. Briefly distinguish the 3 ways in which an organism may be genetically modified (to produce a GMO):

    (a) _____

    (b) _____

    (c) _____

2. On a separate sheet, write a short account describing one of the applications of GMOs described above.

Restriction Enzymes

One of the essential tools of genetic engineering is a group of special **restriction enzymes** (also known as restriction endonucleases). These have the ability to cut DNA molecules at very precise sequences of 4 to 8 base pairs called **recognition sites**. These enzymes are the "molecular scalpels" that allow genetic engineers to cut up DNA in a controlled way. Although first isolated in 1970, these enzymes were discovered earlier in many bacteria (see panel opposite). The purified forms of these bacterial restriction enzymes are used today as tools to cut DNA (see table on the following page for examples). Enzymes are named according to the bacterial species from which they were first isolated. By using a 'tool kit' of over 400 restriction enzymes recognising about 100 recognition sites, genetic engineers can isolate, sequence, and manipulate individual genes derived from any type of organism. The sites at which the fragments of DNA are cut may result in overhanging "sticky ends" or non-overhanging "blunt ends". Pieces may later be joined together using an enzyme called **DNA ligase** in a process called **ligation**.

Sticky End Restriction Enzymes

1 A **restriction enzyme** cuts the double-stranded DNA molecule at its specific **recognition site** (see the table opposite for a representative list of restriction enzymes and their recognition sites).

2 The cuts produce a DNA fragment with two **sticky ends** (ends with exposed nucleotide bases at each end). The piece it is removed from is also left with sticky ends.

Restriction enzymes may cut DNA leaving an overhang or sticky end, without its complementary sequence opposite. DNA cut in such a way is able to be joined to other exposed end fragments of DNA with matching sticky ends. Such joins are specific to their recognition sites.

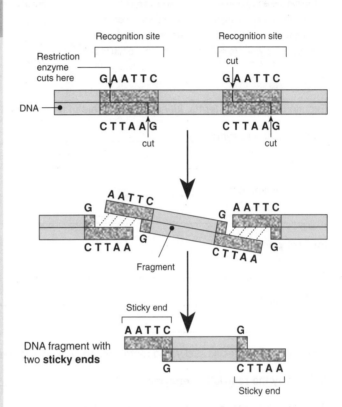

Blunt End Restriction Enzymes

1 A **restriction enzyme** cuts the double-stranded DNA molecule at its specific **recognition site** (see the table opposite for a representative list of restriction enzymes and their recognition sites).

2 The cuts produce a DNA fragment with two **blunt ends** (ends with no exposed nucleotide bases at each end). The piece it is removed from is also left with blunt ends.

It is possible to use restriction enzymes that cut leaving no overhang. DNA cut in such a way is able to be joined to any other blunt end fragment, but tends to be nonspecific because there are no sticky ends as recognition sites.

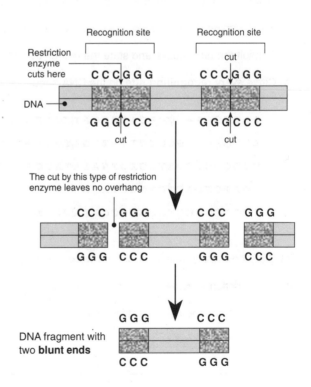

Code: A 3

Origin of Restriction Enzymes

Restriction enzymes have been isolated from many bacteria. It was observed that certain *bacteriophages* (viruses that infect bacteria) could not infect bacteria other than their usual hosts. The reason was found to be that other potential hosts could destroy almost all of the phage DNA using *restriction enzymes* present naturally in their cells; a defence mechanism against the entry of foreign DNA. Restriction enzymes are named according to the species they were first isolated from, followed by a number to distinguish different enzymes isolated from the same organism.

Recognition sites for selected restriction enzymes

Enzyme	Source	Recognition sites
*Eco*RI	*Escherichia coli* RY13	G A A T T C
*Bam*HI	*Bacillus amyloliquefaciens* H	G G A T C C
*Hae*III	*Haemophilus aegyptius*	G G C C
*Hind*III	*Haemophilus influenzae* Rd	A A G C T T
*Hpa*I	*Haemophilus parainfluenzae*	G T T A A C
*Hpa*II	*Haemophilus parainfluenzae*	C C G G
*Mbo*I	*Moraxella bovis*	G A T C
*Not*I	*Norcardia otitidis-caviarum*	G C G G C C G C
*Taq*I	*Thermus aquaticus*	T C G A

1. Explain the following terms, identifying their role in recombinant DNA technology:

   (a) Restriction enzyme: _____

   _____

   (b) Recognition site: _____

   _____

   (c) Sticky end: _____

   _____

   (d) Blunt end: _____

   _____

2. The action of a specific sticky end restriction enzyme is illustrated on the opposite page (top). Use the table above to:

   (a) Identify the **restriction enzyme** used: _____

   (b) Name the organism from which it was first isolated: _____

   (c) State the **base sequence** for this restriction enzyme's recognition site: _____

3. A genetic engineer wants to use the restriction enzyme *Bam*HI to cut the DNA sequence below:

   (a) Consult the table above and state the recognition site for this enzyme: _____

   (b) Circle every **recognition site** on the DNA sequence below that could be cut by the enzyme *Bam*HI:

```
         10              20              30              40              50              60
|AATGGGTACG|CACAGTGGAT|CCACGTAGTA|TGCGATGCGT|AGTGTTTATG|GAGAGAAGAA|
         70              80              90             100             110             120
|AACGCGTCGC|CTTTTATCGA|TGCTGTACGG|ATGCGGAAGT|GGCGATGAGG|ATCCATGCAA|
        130             140             150             160             170             180
|TCGCGGCCGA|TCGXGTAATA|TATCGTGGCT|GCGTTTATTA|TCGTGACTAG|TAGCAGTATG|
        190             200             210             220             230             240
|CGATGTGACT|GATGCTATGC|TGACTATGCT|ATGTTTTTAT|GCTGGATCCA|GCGTAAGCAT|
        250             260             270             280             290             300
|TTCGCTGCGT|GGATCCCATA|TCCTTATATG|CATATATTCT|TATACGGATC|GCGCACGTTT|
```

   (c) State how many fragments of DNA were created by this action: _____

4. When restriction enzymes were first isolated in 1970, there were not many applications to which they could be put to use. Now, they are an important tool in genetic engineering. Describe the human needs and demands that have driven the development and use of restriction enzymes in genetic engineering:

   _____

   _____

   _____

Ligation

DNA fragments produced using restriction enzymes may be reassembled by a process called **ligation**. Pieces are joined together using an enzyme called *DNA ligase*. DNA of different origins produced in this way is called **recombinant DNA** (because it is DNA that has been *recombined* from different sources). The combined techniques of using restriction enzymes and ligation are the basic tools of genetic engineering (also known as recombinant DNA technology).

Creating a Recombinant DNA Plasmid

1 If two pieces of DNA are cut by the same restriction enzyme, they will produce fragments with matching **sticky ends** (ends with exposed nucleotide bases at each end).

2 When two such matching sticky ends come together, they can join by base-pairing. This process is called **annealing**. This can allow DNA fragments from a different source, perhaps a **plasmid**, to be joined to the DNA fragment.

3 The joined fragments will usually form either a linear molecule or a circular one, as shown here for a **plasmid**. However, other combinations of fragments can occur.

4 The fragments of DNA are joined together by the enzyme **DNA ligase**, producing a molecule of **recombinant DNA**.

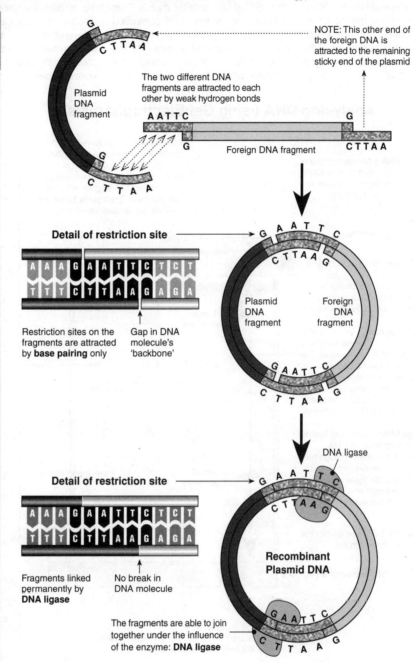

NOTE: This other end of the foreign DNA is attracted to the remaining sticky end of the plasmid

The two different DNA fragments are attracted to each other by weak hydrogen bonds

Plasmid DNA fragment

Foreign DNA fragment

Detail of restriction site

Restriction sites on the fragments are attracted by **base pairing** only

Gap in DNA molecule's 'backbone'

Plasmid DNA fragment

Foreign DNA fragment

DNA ligase

Detail of restriction site

Fragments linked permanently by **DNA ligase**

No break in DNA molecule

Recombinant Plasmid DNA

The fragments are able to join together under the influence of the enzyme: **DNA ligase**

---

1. Explain in your own words the two main steps in the process of joining two DNA fragments together:

   (a) Annealing: _____

   _____

   (b) DNA ligase: _____

   _____

2. Briefly state the **usual role** of DNA ligase in a cell (Hint: Refer to a reference on DNA replication):

   _____

3. Explain why **ligation** can be considered the reverse of the **restriction enzyme** process: _____

   _____

Gel Electrophoresis

Gel electrophoresis is a method that separates large molecules (including nucleic acids or proteins) on the basis of size, electric charge, and other physical properties. Such molecules possess a slight electric charge (see DNA below). To prepare DNA for gel electrophoresis the DNA is often cut up into smaller pieces. This is done by mixing DNA with restriction enzymes in controlled conditions for about an hour. Called **restriction digestion**, it produces a range of DNA fragments of different lengths. During electrophoresis, molecules are forced to move through the pores of a **gel** (a jelly-like material), when the electrical current is applied. Active electrodes at each end of the gel provide the driving force. The electrical current from one electrode repels the molecules while the other electrode simultaneously attracts the molecules. The frictional force of the gel resists the flow of the molecules, separating them by size. Their rate of migration through the gel depends on the strength of the electric field, size and shape of the molecules, and on the ionic strength and temperature of the buffer in which the molecules are moving. After staining, the separated molecules in each lane can be seen as a series of bands spread from one end of the gel to the other.

Analysing DNA using Gel Electrophoresis

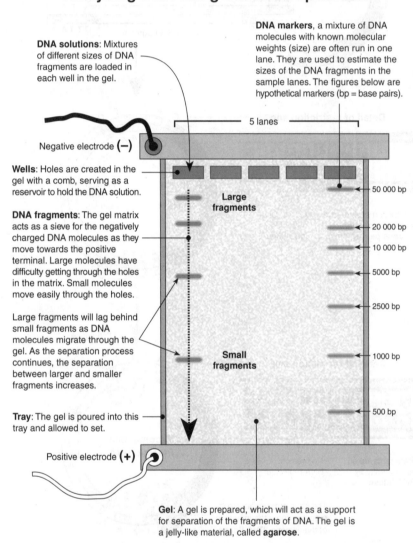

DNA solutions: Mixtures of different sizes of DNA fragments are loaded in each well in the gel.

DNA markers, a mixture of DNA molecules with known molecular weights (size) are often run in one lane. They are used to estimate the sizes of the DNA fragments in the sample lanes. The figures below are hypothetical markers (bp = base pairs).

Negative electrode (−)

Wells: Holes are created in the gel with a comb, serving as a reservoir to hold the DNA solution.

DNA fragments: The gel matrix acts as a sieve for the negatively charged DNA molecules as they move towards the positive terminal. Large molecules have difficulty getting through the holes in the matrix. Small molecules move easily through the holes.

Large fragments will lag behind small fragments as DNA molecules migrate through the gel. As the separation process continues, the separation between larger and smaller fragments increases.

Tray: The gel is poured into this tray and allowed to set.

Positive electrode (+)

Large fragments

Small fragments

5 lanes

50 000 bp
20 000 bp
10 000 bp
5000 bp
2500 bp
1000 bp
500 bp

Gel: A gel is prepared, which will act as a support for separation of the fragments of DNA. The gel is a jelly-like material, called **agarose**.

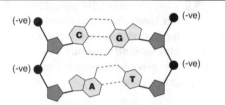

DNA is negatively charged because the phosphates (black) that form part of the backbone of a DNA molecule have a negative charge.

Steps in the process of gel electrophoresis of DNA

1. A tray is prepared to hold the gel matrix.

2. A gel comb is used to create holes in the gel. The gel comb is placed in the tray.

3. Agarose gel powder is mixed with a buffer solution (the liquid used to carry the DNA in a stable form). The solution is heated until dissolved and poured into the tray and allowed to cool.

4. The gel tray is placed in an electrophoresis chamber and the chamber is filled with buffer, covering the gel. This allows the electric current from electrodes at either end of the gel to flow through the gel.

5. DNA samples are mixed with a "loading dye" to make the DNA sample visible. The dye also contains glycerol or sucrose to make the DNA sample heavy so that it will sink to the bottom of the well.

6. A safety cover is placed over the gel, electrodes are attached to a power supply and turned on.

7. When the dye marker has moved through the gel, the current is turned off and the gel is removed from the tray.

8. DNA molecules are made visible by staining the gel with **methylene blue** or ethidium bromide (which binds to DNA and fluoresces in UV light).

---

1. Explain the purpose of gel electrophoresis: _____

_____

_____

2. Describe the two forces that control the speed at which fragments pass through the gel:

   (a) _____

   (b) _____

3. Explain why the smallest fragments travel through the gel the fastest: _____

_____

_____

Polymerase Chain Reaction

Many procedures in DNA technology (such as DNA sequencing and DNA profiling) require substantial amounts of DNA to work with. Some samples, such as those from a crime scene or fragments of DNA from a long extinct organism, may be difficult to get in any quantity. The diagram below describes the laboratory process called **polymerase chain reaction** (**PCR**). Using this technique, vast quantities of DNA identical to trace samples can be created. This process is often termed **DNA amplification**. Although only one cycle of replication is shown below, following cycles replicate DNA at an exponential rate. PCR can be used to make billions of copies in only a few hours.

A Single Cycle of the Polymerase Chain Reaction

DNA polymerase: A thermally stable form of the enzyme is used (e.g. *Taq* polymerase). This is extracted from thermophilic bacteria.

Primer annealed

Primer moving into position

Nucleotides

Direction of synthesis

1 A DNA sample (called target DNA) is obtained. It is **denatured** (DNA strands are separated) by heating at 98°C for 5 minutes.

2 The sample is cooled to 60°C. Primers are **annealed** (bonded) to each DNA strand. In PCR, the primers are short strands of DNA; they provide the starting sequence for DNA extension.

3 Free nucleotides and the enzyme DNA polymerase are added. DNA polymerase binds to the primers and, using the free nucleotides, synthesises complementary strands of DNA.

4 After one cycle, there are now two copies of the original DNA.

Repeat for about 25 cycles

Repeat cycle of heating and cooling until enough copies of the target DNA have been produced

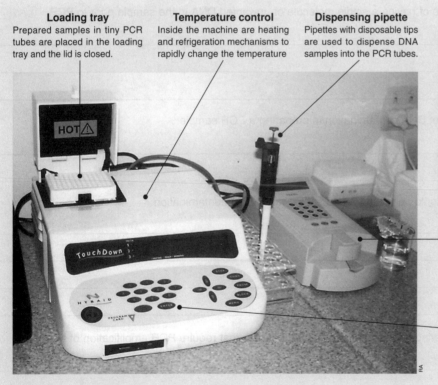

Loading tray
Prepared samples in tiny PCR tubes are placed in the loading tray and the lid is closed.

Temperature control
Inside the machine are heating and refrigeration mechanisms to rapidly change the temperature

Dispensing pipette
Pipettes with disposable tips are used to dispense DNA samples into the PCR tubes.

Thermal Cycler

Amplification of DNA can be carried out with simple-to-use machines called **thermal cyclers**. Once a DNA sample has been prepared, in just a few hours the amount of DNA can be increased billions of times. Thermal cyclers are in common use in the biology departments of universities, as well as other kinds of research and analytical laboratories. The one pictured on the left is typical of this modern piece of equipment.

DNA quantitation
The amount of DNA in a sample can be determined by placing a known volume in this quantitation machine. For many genetic engineering processes, a minimum amount of DNA is required.

Controls
The control panel allows a number of different PCR programmes to be stored in the machine's memory. Carrying out a PCR run usually just involves starting one of the stored programmes.

1. Explain the purpose of PCR: _____

_____

_____

_____

2. Briefly describe how the **polymerase chain reaction** works: _____

_____

_____

_____

_____

_____

_____

_____

3. Describe three situations where only very small DNA samples may be available for sampling and PCR could be used:

(a) _____

_____

(b) _____

_____

(c) _____

_____

4. After only two cycles of replication, four copies of the double-stranded DNA exist. Calculate how much a DNA sample will have increased after:

(a) 10 cycles: _____   (b) 25 cycles: _____

5. The risk of contamination in the preparation for PCR is considerable.

(a) Explain what the effect would be of having a single molecule of unwanted DNA in the sample prior to PCR:

_____

_____

_____

(b) Describe two possible sources of DNA contamination in preparing a PCR sample:

Source 1: _____

Source 2: _____

(c) Describe two precautions that could be taken to reduce the risk of DNA contamination:

Precaution 1: _____

_____

Precaution 2: _____

_____

6. Describe two other genetic engineering/genetic manipulation procedures that require PCR amplification of DNA:

(a) _____

_____

(b) _____

_____

_____

Gene Cloning Using Plasmids

Gene cloning is a process of making large quantities of a desired piece of DNA once it has been isolated. The purpose of this process is often to yield large quantities of either an individual gene or its protein product when the gene is expressed. Methods have been developed to insert a DNA fragment of interest (e.g., a human gene for a desired protein) into the DNA of a vector, resulting in a **recombinant DNA molecule** or **molecular clone**. A **vector** is a self-replicating DNA molecule (e.g. plasmid or viral DNA) used to transmit a gene from one organism into another. To be useful, all vectors must be able to replicate inside their host

organism, they must have one or more sites at which a restriction enzyme can cut, and they must have some kind of genetic marker that allows them to be easily identified. Organisms such as *bacteria, viruses,* and *yeasts* have DNA that behaves in this way. Large quantities of the desired gene can be obtained if the recombinant molecule is allowed to replicate in an appropriate host. The host (e.g. bacterium) may then go on to express the gene and produce the desired protein. Two types of vector are **plasmids** (illustrated below) and **bacteriophages** (viruses that infect bacteria).

Cloning a Human Gene

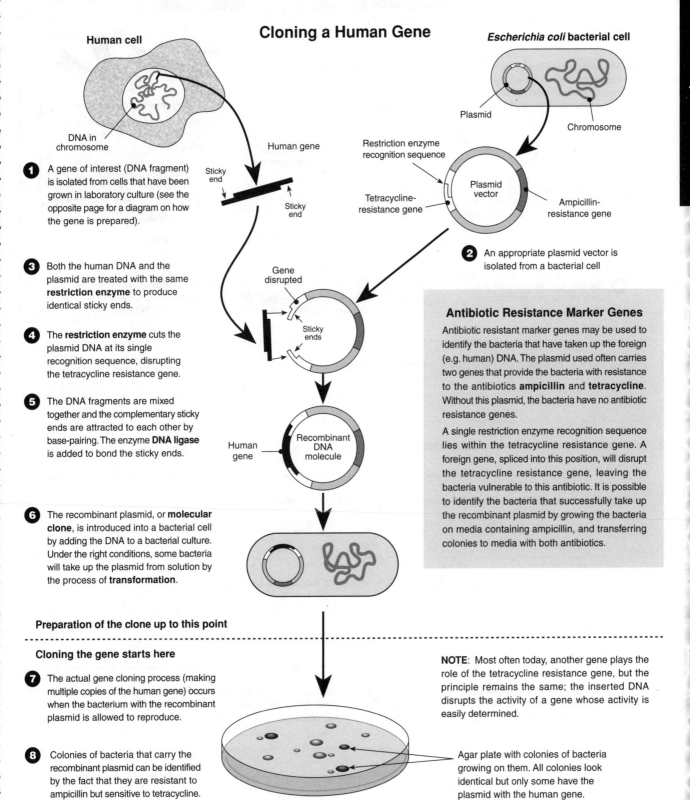

1 A gene of interest (DNA fragment) is isolated from cells that have been grown in laboratory culture (see the opposite page for a diagram on how the gene is prepared).

3 Both the human DNA and the plasmid are treated with the same **restriction enzyme** to produce identical sticky ends.

4 The **restriction enzyme** cuts the plasmid DNA at its single recognition sequence, disrupting the tetracycline resistance gene.

5 The DNA fragments are mixed together and the complementary sticky ends are attracted to each other by base-pairing. The enzyme **DNA ligase** is added to bond the sticky ends.

6 The recombinant plasmid, or **molecular clone**, is introduced into a bacterial cell by adding the DNA to a bacterial culture. Under the right conditions, some bacteria will take up the plasmid from solution by the process of **transformation**.

2 An appropriate plasmid vector is isolated from a bacterial cell

Antibiotic Resistance Marker Genes

Antibiotic resistant marker genes may be used to identify the bacteria that have taken up the foreign (e.g. human) DNA. The plasmid used often carries two genes that provide the bacteria with resistance to the antibiotics **ampicillin** and **tetracycline**. Without this plasmid, the bacteria have no antibiotic resistance genes.

A single restriction enzyme recognition sequence lies within the tetracycline resistance gene. A foreign gene, spliced into this position, will disrupt the tetracycline resistance gene, leaving the bacteria vulnerable to this antibiotic. It is possible to identify the bacteria that successfully take up the recombinant plasmid by growing the bacteria on media containing ampicillin, and transferring colonies to media with both antibiotics.

Preparation of the clone up to this point

- -

Cloning the gene starts here

7 The actual gene cloning process (making multiple copies of the human gene) occurs when the bacterium with the recombinant plasmid is allowed to reproduce.

8 Colonies of bacteria that carry the recombinant plasmid can be identified by the fact that they are resistant to ampicillin but sensitive to tetracycline.

NOTE: Most often today, another gene plays the role of the tetracycline resistance gene, but the principle remains the same; the inserted DNA disrupts the activity of a gene whose activity is easily determined.

Agar plate with colonies of bacteria growing on them. All colonies look identical but only some have the plasmid with the human gene.

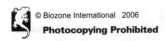

Preparing a Gene For Cloning

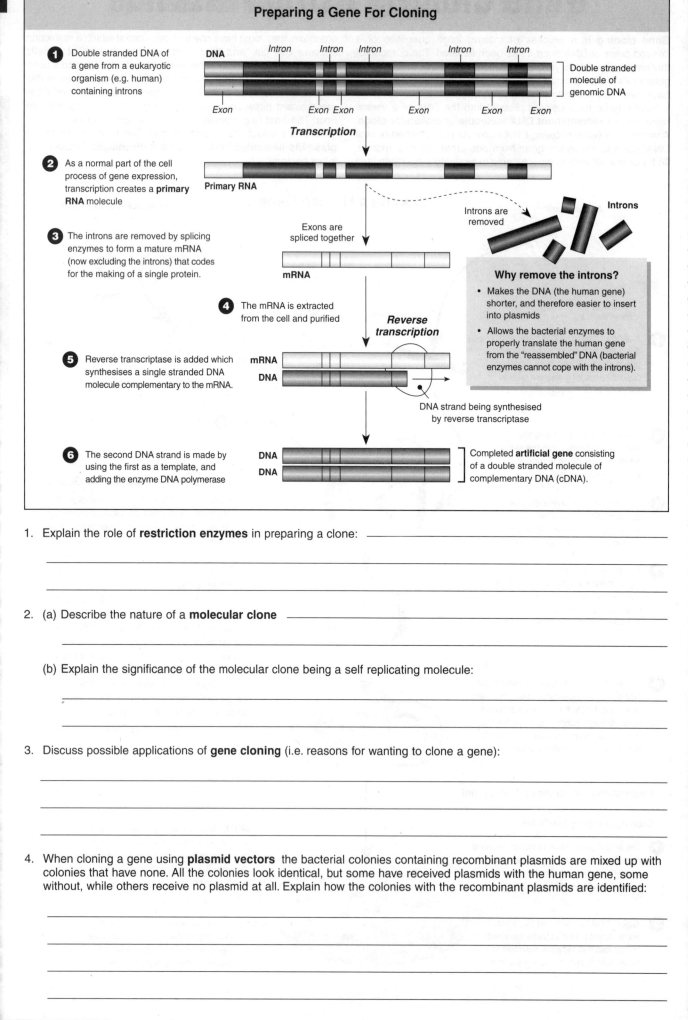

1 Double stranded DNA of a gene from a eukaryotic organism (e.g. human) containing introns

DNA · Intron · Intron · Intron · Intron · Intron

Double stranded molecule of genomic DNA

Exon · Exon Exon · Exon · Exon · Exon

Transcription

2 As a normal part of the cell process of gene expression, transcription creates a **primary RNA** molecule

Primary RNA

Introns are removed

Introns

Exons are spliced together

3 The introns are removed by splicing enzymes to form a mature mRNA (now excluding the introns) that codes for the making of a single protein.

mRNA

Why remove the introns?
• Makes the DNA (the human gene) shorter, and therefore easier to insert into plasmids
• Allows the bacterial enzymes to properly translate the human gene from the "reassembled" DNA (bacterial enzymes cannot cope with the introns).

4 The mRNA is extracted from the cell and purified

Reverse transcription

5 Reverse transcriptase is added which synthesises a single stranded DNA molecule complementary to the mRNA.

mRNA

DNA

DNA strand being synthesised by reverse transcriptase

6 The second DNA strand is made by using the first as a template, and adding the enzyme DNA polymerase

DNA

DNA

Completed **artificial gene** consisting of a double stranded molecule of complementary DNA (cDNA).

1. Explain the role of **restriction enzymes** in preparing a clone: _____

_____

_____

2. (a) Describe the nature of a **molecular clone** _____

_____

(b) Explain the significance of the molecular clone being a self replicating molecule:

_____

_____

3. Discuss possible applications of **gene cloning** (i.e. reasons for wanting to clone a gene):

_____

_____

_____

4. When cloning a gene using **plasmid vectors** the bacterial colonies containing recombinant plasmids are mixed up with colonies that have none. All the colonies look identical, but some have received plasmids with the human gene, some without, while others receive no plasmid at all. Explain how the colonies with the recombinant plasmids are identified:

_____

_____

_____

_____

Transgenic Organisms

Transformation is concerned with the movement of genes from one species to another. An organism developing from a cell into which foreign DNA has been inserted is called a **transgenic organism**. Transgenic techniques have been applied to plants animals, and bacteria. They allow direct modification of a genome and enable traits to be introduced that are not even naturally present in a species. The applications of this technology are various, e.g. improvement of crop yields, production of herbicide resistant plants, enhancement of desirable features in livestock, production of human proteins, and the treatment of genetic defects through **gene therapy**. Cloning technology can be used to propagate transgenic organisms so that introduced genes quickly become part of the germ line (and are inherited). Some methods involved in transformation are shown below:

Liposomes

Liposomes, small spherical vesicles made of a single membrane, can be made commercially to precise specifications. When they are coated with appropriate surface molecules, they are attracted to specific cell types in the body. DNA carried by the liposome can enter the cell by endocytosis or fusion. They can be used to deliver genes to these cells to correct defective or missing genes, providing gene therapy.

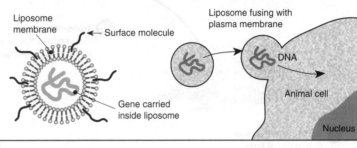

Plasmid Vectors

Plasmids are naturally occurring accessory chromosomes found in bacteria. Plasmids are usually transferred between closely related bacteria by cell-to-cell contact (conjugation). Simple chemical treatments can make mammalian cells, yeast cells and some bacterial cells that do not naturally transfer DNA, take up external, naked DNA. *Agrobacterium tumefaciens* (a bacterium) can insert part of its plasmid directly into plant cells.

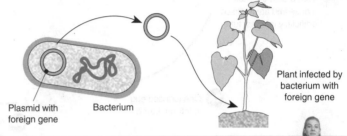

Viral Vectors

Viruses, such as those shown on the right, are well suited for gene therapy. They can accommodate up to 7500 bases of inserted DNA in their protein capsule. When viruses infect and reproduce inside the target cells, they are also spreading the recombinant DNA. They have already been used in several clinical trials of gene therapy for different diseases. A problem with this method involves the host immune reaction to the virus.

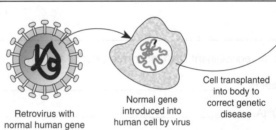

Pronuclear Injection

DNA can be introduced directly into an animal cell by microinjection. Multiple copies of the desired transgene are injected via a glass micropipette into a recently fertilised egg cell, which is then transferred to a surrogate mother. Transgenic mice and livestock are produced in this way, but the process is inefficient: only 2-3% of eggs give rise to transgenic animals and only a proportion of these animals express the added gene adequately.

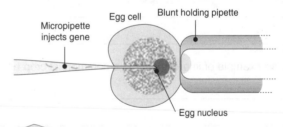

Ballistic DNA Injection

This remarkable way of introducing foreign DNA into living tissue literally shoots it directly into the organism using a "gene gun" (e.g. Helios gene gun made by Bi-Rad). Microscopic particles of gold or tungsten are coated with DNA. They are propelled by a burst of helium into the skin and organs of animals (e.g. rabbit, mouse, pig, fish, etc.) and tissues of intact plants. Some of the cells express the introduced DNA as if it were their own.

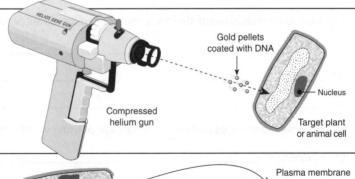

Protoplast Fusion

This process requires the cell walls of plants to be removed by enzymatic digestion. The resulting protoplasts (cells that have lost their cell walls) are then treated with polyethylene glycol which increases their frequency of fusion. In the new hybrid cell, the DNA derived from the two "parent" cells may undergo natural recombination (they may merge).

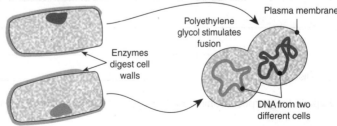

Code: A 3

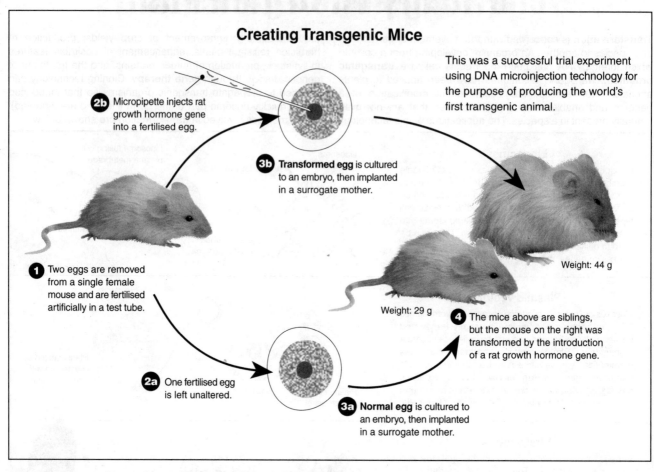

Creating Transgenic Mice

2b Micropipette injects rat growth hormone gene into a fertilised egg.

This was a successful trial experiment using DNA microinjection technology for the purpose of producing the world's first transgenic animal.

3b **Transformed egg** is cultured to an embryo, then implanted in a surrogate mother.

1 Two eggs are removed from a single female mouse and are fertilised artificially in a test tube.

2a One fertilised egg is left unaltered.

3a **Normal egg** is cultured to an embryo, then implanted in a surrogate mother.

Weight: 29 g

Weight: 44 g

4 The mice above are siblings, but the mouse on the right was transformed by the introduction of a rat growth hormone gene.

1. In the context of recombinant DNA technology, define the terms:

   (a) **Transgenesis**: _____

   (b) Foreign DNA: _____

2. Outline the basic principles involved in the production of a **transgenic organism**: _____

   _____

   _____

3. Describe an example of improvement in a commercial crop brought about by the application of transgenic techniques:

   _____

   _____

4. Describe three human needs that have encouraged the development of transgenic techniques:

   (a) _____

   (b) _____

   (c) _____

5. Describe two advantages and one disadvantage of using viruses as vectors for gene delivery:

   (a) Advantages: _____

   _____

   _____

   (b) Disadvantage: _____

6. Explain the purpose behind the transgenic mice experiment (above): _____

   _____

Genetically Modified Plants

Plants with **novel traits** may be produced by traditional methods, such as accelerated mutagenesis or hybridisation. More recently, recombinant DNA techniques and **marker assisted breeding** have allowed a much more controlled and directed approach to introducing new genetic material into plants. Genomic studies of plants, particularly the major crop plants such as rice and wheat, have enabled scientists to identify the genes for particular traits (below) and apply these new technologies to rapidly develop new, high yielding crop varieties. A large number of plants, including many crop plants, have now been genetically modified using recombinant DNA techniques, and the methodology for this (called **transformation**) is now well established (see following page). Scientists are also developing marker assisted breeding technology to move beneficial alleles into modern crop breeding lines through conventional cross breeding. In this method, the allele itself serves as a traceable marker for the trait and seedlings can be scanned for the allele's presence at every round of breeding. This shortens the time it takes to develop a new crop variety. The genetic manipulation of plants through these methods has enabled important agricultural crops to be endowed with new traits that increase yield, improve pest resistance, and reduce the need for agrichemicals.

Matching Traits to Genes in Crop Plants

In crop research, standard mapping techniques can be used to identify the possible location of a gene on a chromosome. Sequencing the DNA in that region enables the gene to then be identified. To find out the gene's function in the plant, scientists can use any one of the techniques described below (A-C).

 Database search

To compare a new desirable gene with those already sequenced in other organisms.

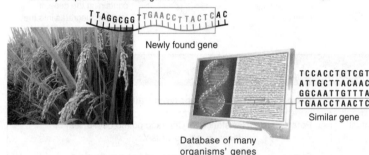

Newly found gene

TCCACCTGTCGT
ATTGCTTACAAC
GGCAATTGTTTA
TGAACCTAACTC

Similar gene

Database of many organisms' genes

The genes responsible for basic cellular activities are often nearly identical in different organisms. A newly found gene can be compared with known genes in existing databases to reveal close matches. 20 000 of the 30 000-50 000 predicted genes in rice have sequence similarity (homology) to previously discovered genes whose function is known.

 Expression profile

To determine when the newly found gene is expressed, hence its probable function.

Microarray of thousands of DNA probes

TGAACCTTACTC

Probe matching the newly found gene

A microarray contains thousands of DNA fragments called probes. Each one matches a mRNA, which acts as a signature for gene activity. When plant cell samples are washed across the microarray, any mRNAs present will stick to their matching probes and fluoresce. If a gene is activated (expressed) at one particular stage of plant development, it is assumed to play a role in that stage.

 Mutant library

To compare the expression of a gene in a normal and a mutant plant in order to determine the function of the newly found gene.

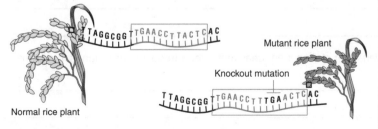

Mutant rice plant

Knockout mutation

Normal rice plant

A small piece of DNA inserted into a gene of interest can "knock out," or silence, that gene in the developing plant. Screening the mutant for differences from normal plants can reveal the gene's usual role.

Desirable Traits

Plant breeders seek to modify traits that lead to increases in yield or improved nutritional value.

Growth	Architecture
Grain size or number	Height
Size of seed head	Branching
Maturation rate	Flowering

Stress tolerance	Nutrient content/quality
Drought	Starch
Pests and diseases	Proteins
Herbicides	Lipids
Intensive fertiliser application	Vitamins

Predicted Classification of Rice Genes

Rice has a relatively small genome compared with other crop plants (430 million bp compared with 3 billion bp in corn and 16 billion bp in wheat). Because of this, it has been the easiest of all the cereals to work with and is the first to have had its entire genome sequenced. The methods described (left) have been already been used to determine (or predict) the functions of a large fraction of the genes in rice.

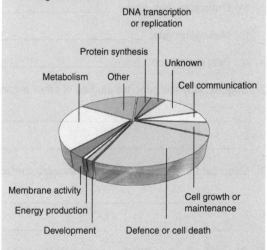

DNA transcription or replication

Protein synthesis

Metabolism   Other

Unknown

Cell communication

Cell growth or maintenance

Membrane activity

Energy production

Development   Defence or cell death

Adapted from: Goff and Salmeron (2004). Back to the future of cereals. Scientific American 291(2), August 2004, pp. 26-33.

Code: RA 2

Transformation using a *Ti* Plasmid in *Agrobacterium*

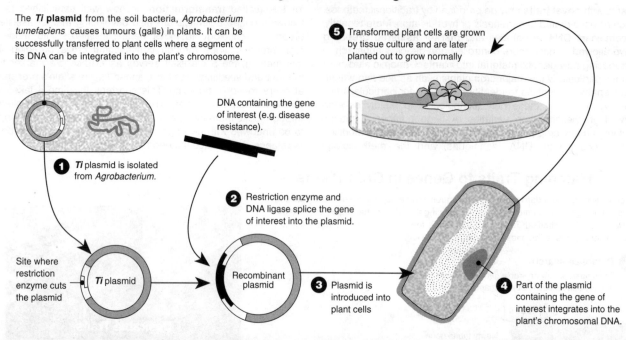

The *Ti* plasmid from the soil bacteria, *Agrobacterium tumefaciens* causes tumours (galls) in plants. It can be successfully transferred to plant cells where a segment of its DNA can be integrated into the plant's chromosome.

5 Transformed plant cells are grown by tissue culture and are later planted out to grow normally

1 *Ti* plasmid is isolated from *Agrobacterium*.

DNA containing the gene of interest (e.g. disease resistance).

2 Restriction enzyme and DNA ligase splice the gene of interest into the plasmid.

Site where restriction enzyme cuts the plasmid

Ti plasmid

Recombinant plasmid

3 Plasmid is introduced into plant cells

4 Part of the plasmid containing the gene of interest integrates into the plant's chromosomal DNA.

Examples of Genetically Modified Plants

Crop	Phenotypic trait altered	Crop	Phenotypic trait altered
Argentine canola	Herbicide tolerance, modified seed fatty acid content (high oleic acid/low linolenic acid expression), pollination control system (male sterility, fertility restoration).	Potato	Resistance to: Colorado potato beetle, leafroll *luteovirus*, potato virus Y.
		Rice	Herbicide resistance, adding provitamin A.
Carnation	Increased shelf-life (delayed senescence), herbicide tolerance, modified flower colour.	Soybean	Herbicide resistance, modified fatty acid content (high oleic acid/low linolenic acid expression), herbicide tolerance.
Chicory	Male sterility, herbicide tolerance.		
Cotton	Herbicide tolerance, resistance to lepidopteran pests (e.g. cotton worm, pink bollworm, tobacco budworm).	Squash	Resistance to infection: cucumber mosaic virus, watermelon mosaic virus, zucchini yellow mosaic virus.
Flax (linseed)	Herbicide tolerance.	Sugar beet	Herbicide tolerance.
Maize	Herbicide tolerance, male sterility, resistance to European corn borer.	Tobacco	Herbicide tolerance.
		Tomato	Increased shelf-life through delayed ripening and delayed softening. Resistance to lepidopteran pests.
Melon	Delayed ripening.		
Papaya	Resistance to infection by papaya ringspot virus.	Wheat	Herbicide tolerance.

1. For each of the following traits, suggest features that could be desirable in terms of increasing yield:

   (a) Grain size or number: _____

   (b) Maturation rate: _____

   (c) Pest resistance: _____

2. Suggest why the genomic studies of other organisms are still useful in terms of identifying gene functions in crop plants:

   _____

   _____

3. Describe the property of *Agrobacterium tumefaciens* that makes it an ideal vector for introducing new genes into plants:

   _____

   _____

4. Suggest why a modified protein content might be desirable in a food crop: _____

   _____

Using Recombinant Bacteria

In 1990 Pfizer, Inc. produced one of the first two products of recombinant DNA technology to enter the human food supply: the "CHY-MAX" brand of chymosin. This was a protein purified from bacteria that had been given a copy of the chymosin gene from cattle. Traditionally extracted from "chyme" or stomach secretions of suckling calves, chymosin (also called rennin) is an enzyme that digests milk proteins. Chymosin is the active ingredient in rennet, used by cheesemakers to clot milk into curds. CHY-MAX extracted from bacteria grown in a vat is identical in chemical composition to the chymosin extracted from cattle. Pfizer's product quickly won over half the market for rennet because cheesemakers found it to be a cost-effective source of high-quality chymosin in consistent supply. A recombinant form of the fungus, *Mucor*, is also used to manufacture chymosin.

Chymosin Production using Recombinant Bacteria

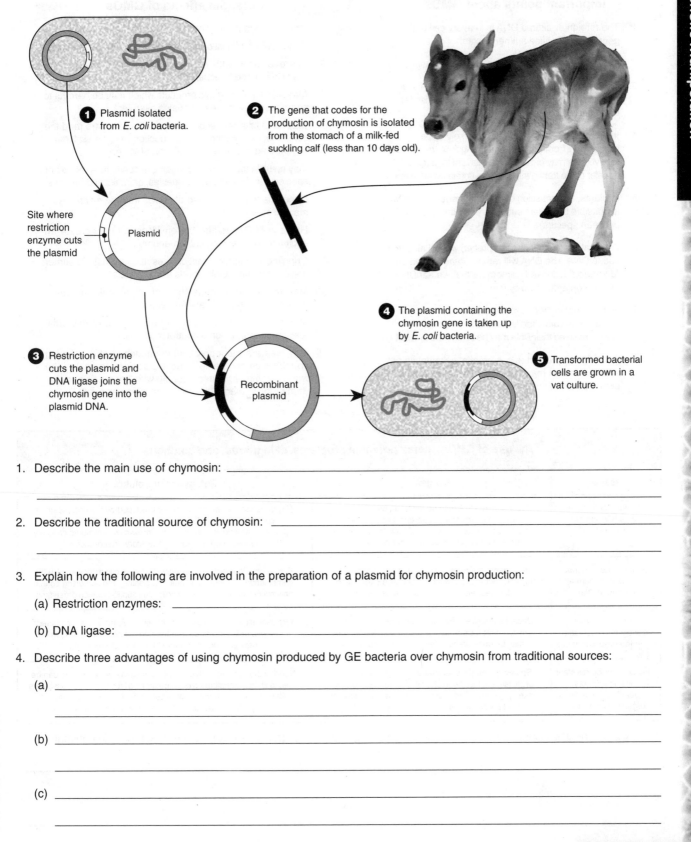

1 Plasmid isolated from *E. coli* bacteria.

2 The gene that codes for the production of chymosin is isolated from the stomach of a milk-fed suckling calf (less than 10 days old).

Site where restriction enzyme cuts the plasmid

Plasmid

3 Restriction enzyme cuts the plasmid and DNA ligase joins the chymosin gene into the plasmid DNA.

Recombinant plasmid

4 The plasmid containing the chymosin gene is taken up by *E. coli* bacteria.

5 Transformed bacterial cells are grown in a vat culture.

1. Describe the main use of chymosin: _____
    _____

2. Describe the traditional source of chymosin: _____
    _____

3. Explain how the following are involved in the preparation of a plasmid for chymosin production:

    (a) Restriction enzymes: _____

    (b) DNA ligase: _____

4. Describe three advantages of using chymosin produced by GE bacteria over chymosin from traditional sources:

    (a) _____
        _____

    (b) _____
        _____

    (c) _____
        _____

The Ethics of GMO Technology

The risks of using **genetically modified organisms** (GMOs) have been the subject of considerable debate in recent times. Most experts agree that, provided GMOs are tested properly, the health risks to individuals should be minimal from plant products, although minor problems may occur. Health risks from animal GMOs are potentially more serious, especially when the animals are for human consumption. The potentially huge benefits to be gained from the use of GMOs creates enormous pressure to apply the existing technology. However, there are many concerns, including the environmental and socio-economic effects, and problems of unregulated use. There is also concern about the environmental and economic costs of possible GMO accidents. GMO research is being driven by heavy investment on the part of biotechnology companies seeking new applications for GMOs. Currently a matter of great concern to consumers is the adequacy of government regulations for the labelling of food products with GMO content. This may have important trade implications for countries exporting and importing GMO produce.

Important points about GMOs

1. The foreign or altered DNA is in every cell of the genetically modified animal or plant.

2. The mRNA is only expressed in specific tissues.

3. The foreign protein is only expressed in those tissues but it may circulate (e.g. hormone in the bloodstream) or be secreted (e.g. milk).

4. In animals, the transgene is only likely to be transmitted from parent to offspring (but the use of viral vectors may provide a mechanism for accidental transfer of the transgene between unrelated animals).

5. In plants, transmission of the transgene in GMOs is possible by pollen, cuttings, and seeds (even between species).

6. If we eat the animal or plant proper, we will also be eating DNA. The DNA will remain 'intact' if raw, but "degraded" if cooked (remember that we eat DNA in our regular food every day).

7. Non-transgenic food products may be processed using genetically modified bacteria or yeast, and cells containing their DNA may be in the food product.

8. A transgenic product (e.g. a protein, polypeptide or a carbohydrate) may be in the GMO, but not in the portions sold to the consumer.

Potential effects of GMOs

1. Increase food production.

2. Decrease use of pesticides, herbicides and animal remedies.

3. Improve the health of the human population and the medicines used to achieve it.

4. May result in transgenic products which may be harmful to some (e.g. new proteins causing allergies).

5. May have little real economic benefit to farmers (and the consumer) when increased production (as little as 10%) is weighed against cost, capital, competition.

6. May result in transgenes spreading uncontrollably into other species: plants, indigenous species, animals, and humans.

7. Concerns that the release of GMOs into the environment may be irreversible.

8. Release of GMOs into the environment may create an evolutionary or ecological "timebomb".

9. Crippling economic sanctions resulting from a consumer backlash against GMO foods and products.

10. May make the animals that are genetically modified unhealthy (animal welfare and ethical issues).

11. May cause the emergence of pest, insect, or microbial resistance to traditional control methods.

12. May create a monopoly and dependence of developing countries on companies who are seeking to control the world's commercial seed supply with "terminator seeds" (that produce plants that cannot themselves seed).

The use of GMOs: some potential problems, safeguards, and solutions

Issue	Problem	Safeguard or solution
Accidental release of GMOs into the environment	Recombinant DNA may be taken up by non-target, organisms. e.g. weeds may take up a gene for herbicide resistance. These unintended GMOs may have the potential to become pests or cause disease.	Rigorous standards of control are produced by the organisations in control of GM regulation in each country. GMOs may have specific genes deleted so that their growth requirements can only be met under particular laboratory environments.
A new gene or genes may disrupt normal gene function	In humans, gene disruption may trigger cancer. In animals, successful transformation and expression of the desired gene is frequently very low.	Future developments in producing transgenic livestock involve the combination of genetic engineering, cloning, and screening so that only successfully transformed cells are used to produce organisms.
Targeted use of transgenic organisms in the environment	Once their desired function in the environment, e.g., environmental clean-up, has been completed, they may be undesirable invaders in the ecosystem	Organisms can be engineered to contain "suicide genes" or inherent metabolic deficiencies so that they do not survive for long in the new environment after completion of their task.
Use of antibiotic resistant genes as markers to identify transgenic organisms in culture	Spread of antibiotic resistance amongst non-target organisms. It has been shown that gut bacteria can take up genes for antibiotic resistance from ingested food products (e.g. wheat and soy products).	None, although alternative methods, such as gene probes, can be used to identify transformed cells. Better food labelling helps consumers identify foods made from GMOs but, even with this precaution, the problem has not been adequately addressed.

1. Suggest why genetically modified (GM) plants are thought to pose a greater environmental threat than GM animals:

_____

_____

_____

2. Describe an advantage and a problem with the use of genetically engineered herbicide resistant crop plants:

(a) Advantage: _____

_____

(b) Problem: _____

_____

3. Describe an advantage and a problem with using tropical crops genetically engineered to grow in cold regions:

(a) Advantage: _____

_____

(b) Problem: _____

_____

4. Describe an advantage and a problem with using crops that are genetically engineered to grow in marginal habitats (for example, in very saline or poorly aerated soils):

(a) Advantage: _____

_____

(b) Problem: _____

_____

5. Describe two uses of transgenic animals within the livestock industry:

(a) _____

(b) _____

6. Recently, Britain banned the import of a genetically engineered, pest resistant corn variety containing marker genes for ampicillin antibiotic resistance. Suggest why there was concern over using such marker genes:

_____

_____

7. Many agricultural applications of DNA technology make use of transgenic bacteria which infect plants and express a foreign gene. Explain one advantage of each of the following applications of genetic engineering to crop biology:

(a) Development of nitrogen-fixing *Rhizobium* bacteria that can colonise non-legumes such as corn and wheat:

_____

(b) Addition of transgenic *Pseudomonas flourescens* bacteria into seeds (bacterium produces a pathogen-killing toxin):

_____

8. Some of the public's fears and concerns about genetically modified food stem from moral or religious convictions, while others have a biological basis and are related to the potential biological threat posed by GMOs.
(a) Conduct a class discussion or debate to identify these fears and concerns, and list them below:

_____

_____

_____

_____

(b) Identify which of those you have listed above pose a real biological threat: _____

_____

_____

_____

Biotechnology in Medicine

Techniques and applications of biotechnology in medicine and healthcare

Monoclonal antibodies, proteins and pharmaceuticals, conventional and GE vaccines, and gene therapy.

Learning Objectives

☐ 1. Compile your own glossary from the **KEY WORDS** displayed in **bold type** in the learning objectives below.

Medical Biotechnology (pages 51-52, 79-80)

☐ 2. Discuss one or more of the following with reference to both technique and practical application:
   (a) **Monoclonal antibodies**
   (b) **Tissue engineering**
   (c) **Stem cell cloning**

Pharmaceuticals (pages 60, 73, 77-78, 81-83)

☐ 3. Describe the role of **gene cloning** and **industrial-scale fermentation** technology in the mass production of valuable commodities such as:
   (a) Human proteins, including hormones, e.g. human **insulin**, **factor VIII**, and human growth hormone.
   (b) Vitamins, enzymes, and dietary supplements.
   (c) Pharmaceuticals such as antibiotics and **vaccines**.

☐ 4. Describe the use of transgenic livestock to produce human proteins, such as **alpha-1-antitrypsin** and **interferon**. Discuss the medical applications of these (and other) proteins.

☐ 5. Describe the advantages (over traditional methods) of using recombinant DNA technology to produce valuable commodities, such as human proteins. Explain how this application of gene technology can meet human needs safely, efficiently, and at relatively low cost. Using examples, evaluate any disadvantages with reference to traditional methods of production.

☐ 6. Describe the principles involved in the production of a **vaccine**. Distinguish between **subunit** and **whole-agent vaccines** and between **inactivated** (dead) and **live** (attenuated) **vaccines**. Contrast the risks and benefits associated with live and dead vaccines.

☐ 7. Explain the production and application of **recombinant DNA vaccines**, identifying existing and future benefits of these over vaccines produced by traditional methods.

Gene therapy (pages 84-87)

☐ 8. Outline the principles of **gene therapy**. Identify the criteria that must be met before gene therapy can be considered as a potentially viable treatment. Distinguish between using gene therapy to cure a disease and its use to relieve symptoms of a disease.

☐ 9. Describe the genetic basis of **cystic fibrosis** (CF) and the symptoms of the disease that arise as a result of this defect. In terms of its genetic basis, explain the potential for CF to be treated/cured using gene therapy.

☐ 10. Using an appropriate example, explain the techniques involved in **gene therapy**, including the **vectors** used, and delivery systems for these vectors. With reference to your specific example, discuss the difficulties currently encountered in improving the success of gene therapy and explain why successful gene therapy has, to date, been largely unsuccessful.

☐ 11. Identify types of **vectors** used in gene therapy and discuss the advantages and disadvantages of each. Include reference to **viral vectors** and **liposomes**.

 Supplementary Texts

See page 8 for additional details of these texts:
- Chenn, P., 1997. **Microorganisms and Biotechnology** (John Murray), chpt 8-9.
- Freeland, P., 1999. **Microbes, Medicine and Commerce** (Hodder and Stoughton), chpt 3 & 6.
- Jones, N., et al., 2001. **The Essentials of Genetics** (John Murray), chpt 18.
- Lowrie, P., et al., 2000. **Microbiology and Biotechnology** (Cambridge University Press), chpt 4-5.
- Taylor, J., 2001. **Microorganisms and Biotechnology** (NelsonThornes), chpt 6.

  Periodicals

See page 8 for details of publishers of periodicals:
- **Genes Can Come True** New Scientist, 30 Nov. 2002, pp. 30-33. *An overview of the current state of gene therapy, and a note about future directions.*
- **First Gene Therapy Approved** New Scientist, 29 Nov. 2003, p. 13. *For the first time, a gene therapy treatment has been approved by regulatory authorities. It consists of using an adenoviral vector to insert a p53 gene, coding for a protein that triggers cell suicide and attacks tumours.*
- **Making Gene Therapy Work** Scientific American, June 1997, pp. 79-103. *Thorough coverage of gene therapy technologies.*
- **Edible Vaccines** Scientific American, Sept. 2000, pp. 48-53. *Vaccines in food may be the way of future immunisation programmes.*
- **Made to Measure Drugs** Biol. Sci. Rev., 14(4) April 2002, pp. 34-36. *The technical and ethical issues associated with the use of HGP information for the design of new drugs for individuals.*

- **Defensive Eating** Scientific American, May. 2005, pp. 13-14. *Food vaccines developed as pills.*
- **Tailor-Made Proteins** Biol. Sci. Rev., 13(4) March 2001, pp. 2-6. *Recombinant proteins and their uses in industry and medicine.*
- **Proteins Rule** Scientific American, April 2002, pp. 27-33. *After the HGP, the race is on to catalogue human proteins and their functions.*
- **Insulin from Yeast** Biol. Sci. Rev., 10(2) Nov. 1997, pp. 30-32. *Genetic engineering to produce human insulin for the treatment of diabetes.*

 Internet

See pages 4-5 for details of how to access **Bio Links** from our web site: **www.thebiozone.com** From Bio Links, access sites under the topics:
BIOTECHNOLOGY > Applications > Medical biotechnology: Gene therapy: An overview • Transfer and cloning of the insulin gene
HEALTH & DISEASE > Prevention and Treatment • Monoclonal antibodies ... and others

Production of Human Proteins

Transgenic microorganisms are now widely used as **biofactories** for the production of human proteins. These proteins are often used to treat metabolic protein-deficiency disorders. **Type I diabetes mellitus** is a metabolic disease caused by a lack of insulin and is treatable only with insulin injection. Before the advent of genetic engineering, insulin was extracted from the pancreatic tissue of pigs or cattle. This method was expensive and problematic in that the insulin caused various side effects and was often contaminated. Since the 1980s, human insulin has been mass produced using genetically modified (GM) bacteria (*Escherichia coli*) and yeast (*Saccharomyces cerevisiae*). Similar methods are used for the genetic manipulation of both microorganisms, although the size of the bacterial plasmid requires that the human gene be inserted as two, separately expressed, nucleotide sequences (see below). The use of insulin from GM sources has greatly improved the management of Type I diabetes, and the range of formulations now available has allowed diabetics to live much more normal lives than previously.

Synthesis of human insulin using recombinant DNA technology

Type I diabetes is treated with regular injections of insulin according to daily needs (right). Since the 1980s, human insulin has been mass produced using genetically modified (GM) microorganisms and marketed under various trade names. Various methodologies are employed to produce the insulin, but all involve inserting a human gene into a plasmid (bacterial or yeast), followed by secretion of a protein product from which the active insulin can be derived.

1 Identify and synthesise the human gene

Insulin is a small, simple protein. It comprises a total of 51 amino acids in two polypeptide chains (A and B). The two chains are linked by disulfide bonds. The nucleotide sequence of the gene for human insulin has been determined from the amino acid sequence. The first step in insulin production is to chemically synthesise the DNA chains that carry the specific nucleotide sequences for the A and B chains of insulin (the A and B 'genes').

2 Insert the synthetic DNA into plasmids

Using a tool kit of restriction enzymes and DNA ligase, the synthetic A and B nucleotide sequences are separately inserted into the gene for the bacterial enzyme, β-galactosidase, which is carried on the bacterial plasmid. In *E. coli*, β-galactosidase controls the transcription of genes. To make the bacteria produce insulin, the insulin gene needs to be tied to the gene for this enzyme.

3 Insert plasmid into the bacterial cell

The recombinant plasmids are then introduced to *E. coli* cells in culture conditions that favour the bacterial uptake of plasmid DNA. In practical terms, the synthesis of human insulin requires millions of copies of bacteria whose plasmid has been combined with the insulin gene. The insulin gene is expressed as it replicates with the β-galactosidase in the cell undergoing mitosis.

4 Make the functional protein

The protein formed consists partly of β-galactosidase, joined either to the A or B chain of insulin. The A and B chains are then extracted from the β-galactosidase fragment and purified. The two chains are then mixed and reconnected in a reaction that forms the disulfide cross bridges and the functional human protein, insulin. The final purified product is made suitable for injection and provided in a number of different formulations.

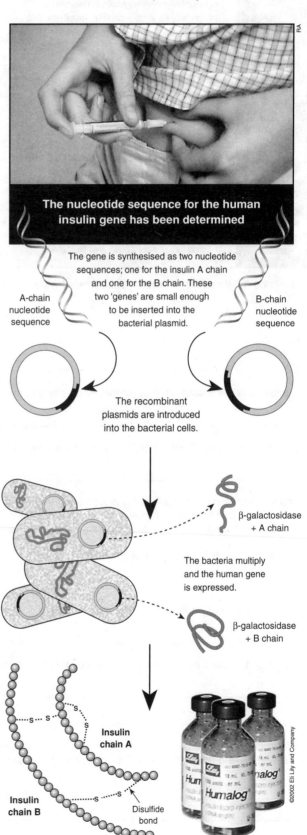

The nucleotide sequence for the human insulin gene has been determined

The gene is synthesised as two nucleotide sequences; one for the insulin A chain and one for the B chain. These two 'genes' are small enough to be inserted into the bacterial plasmid.

A-chain nucleotide sequence

B-chain nucleotide sequence

The recombinant plasmids are introduced into the bacterial cells.

β-galactosidase + A chain

The bacteria multiply and the human gene is expressed.

β-galactosidase + B chain

Insulin chain A

Insulin chain B

Disulfide bond

RA

©2002 Eli Lily and Company

Biotechnology in Medicine

Code: A 3

Human Proteins Produced Using Genetic Engineering

Human protein and biological role	Traditional production method	Current production
Erythropoetin A hormone, produced by kidneys, which stimulates red blood cell production. Used to treat anaemia in patients with kidney failure.	Not applicable. Previous methods to treat anaemia in patients with kidney failure was through repeated blood transfusions.	Cloned gene grown in hamster ovary cells
Human Growth Hormone Pituitary hormone promoting normal growth in height (deficiency results in dwarfism). Injection used to treat pituitary dwarfism.	Extracted from the pituitary glands of corpses. Many patients developed Creutzfeldt-Jacob disease (CJD) as a result. CJD is a degenerative brain disease, transmitted via infected tissues or their extracts.	Genetically engineered bacteria
Insulin Regulates the uptake of glucose by cells. Used (via injection) in the treatment of Type I (insulin-dependent) diabetes mellitus.	Physical extraction from the pancreatic tissue of pigs or cattle. Problems included high cost, sample contamination, and severe side effects.	Genetically engineered bacteria or yeast
Interferon Anti-viral substance produced by virus-infected cells. Used in the treatment of hepatitis B and C, some cancers, and multiple sclerosis.	Not applicable. Relatively recent discovery of the role of these proteins in human physiology.	Genetically engineered bacteria
Factor VIII One of the blood clotting factors normally present in blood. Used in the treatment of haemophilia caused by lack of factor VIII.	Blood donation. Risks of receiving blood contaminated with infective viruses (HIV, hepatitis), despite better screening procedures.	Genetically engineered bacteria

1. Describe the three major problems associated with the traditional method of obtaining insulin to treat diabetes:

   (a) _____

   (b) _____

   (c) _____

2. Explain why the insulin gene is synthesised as two separate A and B chain nucleotide sequences: _____

   _____

3. Explain why the synthetic nucleotide sequences ('genes') are inserted into the β-galactosidase gene: _____

   _____

4. Yeast (*Saccharomyces cerevisiae*) is also used in the production of human insulin. It is a eukaryote with a larger plasmid than *E. coli*. Its secretory pathways are more similar to those of humans and β-galactosidase is not involved in gene expression. **Predict** how these differences might change the procedure for insulin production with respect to:

   (a) Insertion of the gene into the plasmid: _____

   _____

   (b) Secretion and purification of the protein product: _____

   _____

5. Describe the benefits to patients of using GMOs to produce human proteins: _____

   _____

   _____

6. When delivered to a patient, artificially produced human proteins only alleviate disease symptoms; they cannot cure the disease. Give a brief statement describing how this situation might change in the future:

   _____

   _____

   _____

Monoclonal Antibodies

A **monoclonal antibody** is an artificially produced antibody that binds to and inactivates only one specific protein (antigen). Monoclonal antibodies are produced in the laboratory by stimulating the production of B-lymphocytes in mice injected with the antigen. These B-lymphocytes produce an antibody against the antigen. When isolated and made to fuse with immortal tumour cells, they can be cultured indefinitely in a suitable growing medium (as shown below). Monoclonal antibodies are useful for three reasons: they are totally uniform (i.e. clones), they

can be produced in very large quantities at low cost, and they are highly specific. The uses of antibodies produced by this method range from diagnostic tools, to treatments for infections and cancer, and prevention of tissue rejection in transplant patients. Many of the diagnostic tests, e.g. for some sexually transmitted or parasitic infections, previously required relatively difficult culturing or microscopic methods for diagnosis. In addition, newer diagnostic test using monoclonal antibodies are easier to interpret and often require fewer highly trained personnel.

Making Monoclonal Antibodies

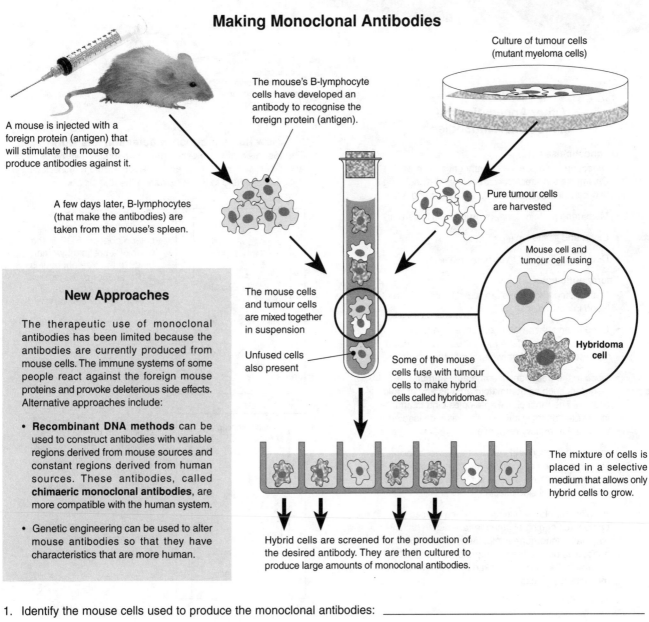

Culture of tumour cells (mutant myeloma cells)

A mouse is injected with a foreign protein (antigen) that will stimulate the mouse to produce antibodies against it.

The mouse's B-lymphocyte cells have developed an antibody to recognise the foreign protein (antigen).

A few days later, B-lymphocytes (that make the antibodies) are taken from the mouse's spleen.

Pure tumour cells are harvested

The mouse cells and tumour cells are mixed together in suspension

Unfused cells also present

Mouse cell and tumour cell fusing

Hybridoma cell

Some of the mouse cells fuse with tumour cells to make hybrid cells called hybridomas.

The mixture of cells is placed in a selective medium that allows only hybrid cells to grow.

Hybrid cells are screened for the production of the desired antibody. They are then cultured to produce large amounts of monoclonal antibodies.

New Approaches

The therapeutic use of monoclonal antibodies has been limited because the antibodies are currently produced from mouse cells. The immune systems of some people react against the foreign mouse proteins and provoke deleterious side effects. Alternative approaches include:

• **Recombinant DNA methods** can be used to construct antibodies with variable regions derived from mouse sources and constant regions derived from human sources. These antibodies, called **chimaeric monoclonal antibodies**, are more compatible with the human system.

• Genetic engineering can be used to alter mouse antibodies so that they have characteristics that are more human.

Biotechnology in Medicine

1. Identify the mouse cells used to produce the monoclonal antibodies: _____

2. Describe the characteristic of tumour cells that allows an ongoing culture of antibody-producing lymphocytes to be made:

_____
_____

3. Compare the method of producing monoclonal antibodies using mice with the alternative methods now available:

_____
_____
_____
_____

Code: RA 2

Detecting Pregnancy using Monoclonal Antibodies

When a woman becomes pregnant, a hormone called **human chorionic gonadotropin** (HCG) is released from the placenta. HCG accumulates in the bloodstream and is excreted in the urine. HCG is a glycoprotein, which means antibodies can be produced against it and used in simple test kits (below) to determine if a woman is pregnant. Monoclonal antibodies are also used in other home testing kits, such as those for detecting ovulation time (far left).

Coloured band appears in control window to show the test has run correctly.

Coloured band appears in the result window only if HCG is present.

Dipstick held in the urine.

How home pregnancy detection kits work

The test area of the dipstick (below) contains two types of antibodies: free monoclonal antibodies and capture monoclonal antibodies, bound to the substrate in the test window.

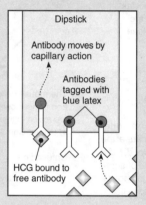

Dipstick

Antibody moves by capillary action

Antibodies tagged with blue latex

HCG bound to free antibody

The free antibodies are specific for HCG and are colour-labelled. HCG in the urine of a pregnant woman binds to the free antibodies on the surface of the dipstick. The antibodies then travel up the dipstick by capillary action.

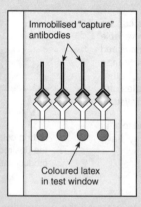

Immobilised "capture" antibodies

Coloured latex in test window

The capture antibodies are specific for the HCG-free antibody complex. The HCG-free antibody complexes travelling up the dipstick are bound by the immobilised **"capture" antibodies**, forming a sandwich. The colour labelled antibodies then create a visible colour change in the test window.

Other Applications of Monoclonal Antibodies

Diagnostic uses

- Detecting the presence of pathogens such as *Chlamydia* and streptococcal bacteria, distinguishing between *Herpesvirus* I and II, and diagnosing AIDS.

- Measuring protein, toxin, or drug levels in serum.

- Blood and tissue typing.

- Detection of antibiotic residues in milk.

Therapeutic uses

- Neutralising endotoxins produced by bacteria in blood infections.

- Used to prevent organ rejection, e.g. in kidney transplants, by interfering with the T cells involved with the rejection of transplanted tissue.

- Used in the treatment of some auto-immune disorders such as rheumatoid arthritis and allergic asthma. The monoclonal antibodies bind to and inactivate factors involved in the cascade leading to the inflammatory response.

- Immunodetection and immunotherapy of cancer. Newer methods specifically target the cell membranes of tumour cells, shrinking solid tumours without harmful side effects.

- Inhibition of platelet clumping, which is used to prevent reclogging of coronary arteries in patients who have undergone angioplasty. The monoclonal antibodies bind to the receptors on the platelet surface that are normally linked by fibrinogen during the clotting process.

4. For each of the following applications, suggest why an antibody-based test or therapy is so valuable:

(a) Detection of toxins or bacteria in perishable foods: _____

_____

_____

(b) Detection of pregnancy without a doctor's prescription: _____

_____

(c) Targeted treatment of tumours in cancer patients: _____

_____

Types of Vaccine

There are two basic types of vaccine: subunit vaccines and whole-agent vaccines. **Whole-agent vaccines** contain complete nonvirulent microbes, either **inactivated** (killed), or alive but **attenuated** (weakened). Attenuated viruses make very effective vaccines and often provide life-long immunity without the need for booster immunisations. Killed viruses are less effective and many vaccines of this sort have now been replaced by newer subunit vaccines. **Subunit vaccines** contain only the parts of the pathogen that induce the immune response. They are safer than attenuated vaccines because they cannot reproduce in the recipient, and they produce fewer adverse effects because they contain little or no extra material. Subunit vaccines can be made using a variety of methods, including cell fragmentation (*acellular vaccines*), inactivation of toxins (*toxoids*), genetic engineering (*recombinant vaccines*), and combination with antigenic proteins (*conjugated vaccines*). In all cases, the subunit vaccine loses its ability to cause disease but retains its antigenic properties so that it remains effective in inducing an immune response. Vaccine-like properties can even be established in recombinant foods containing the genes for antigenic proteins. Some of the most promising vaccines being developed are DNA vaccines; naked DNA which produces an antigenic protein when injected. The safety of DNA vaccines is uncertain but they show promise for use against rapidly mutating viruses such as influenza.

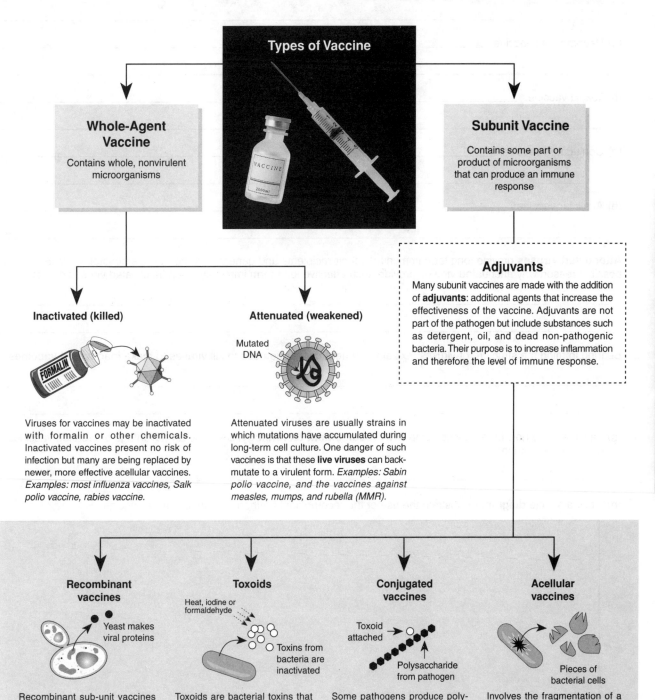

Types of Vaccine

Whole-Agent Vaccine

Contains whole, nonvirulent microorganisms

Subunit Vaccine

Contains some part or product of microorganisms that can produce an immune response

Adjuvants

Many subunit vaccines are made with the addition of **adjuvants**: additional agents that increase the effectiveness of the vaccine. Adjuvants are not part of the pathogen but include substances such as detergent, oil, and dead non-pathogenic bacteria. Their purpose is to increase inflammation and therefore the level of immune response.

Inactivated (killed)

Viruses for vaccines may be inactivated with formalin or other chemicals. Inactivated vaccines present no risk of infection but many are being replaced by newer, more effective acellular vaccines. *Examples: most influenza vaccines, Salk polio vaccine, rabies vaccine.*

Attenuated (weakened)

Mutated DNA

Attenuated viruses are usually strains in which mutations have accumulated during long-term cell culture. One danger of such vaccines is that these **live viruses** can back-mutate to a virulent form. *Examples: Sabin polio vaccine, and the vaccines against measles, mumps, and rubella (MMR).*

Recombinant vaccines

Yeast makes viral proteins

Recombinant sub-unit vaccines can be made using genetic engineering techniques, where non-pathogenic microbes (yeast and bacteria) are programmed to make a desired antigenic fraction. *Example: hepatitis B vaccine.*

Toxoids

Heat, iodine or formaldehyde

Toxins from bacteria are inactivated

Toxoids are bacterial toxins that have been inactivated by heat or chemicals. When injected, the toxoid stimulates the production of antitoxins (antibodies) that neutralise any circulating toxin. *Examples: diphtheria vaccine, tetanus vaccine.*

Conjugated vaccines

Toxoid attached

Polysaccharide from pathogen

Some pathogens produce poly-saccharide capsules that are poorly antigenic, especially in young children. To enhance their effectiveness, they are combined with proteins such as toxoids from other pathogens. *Example: vaccine against Haemophilus influenzae b.*

Acellular vaccines

Pieces of bacterial cells

Involves the fragmentation of a conventional whole-agent vaccine and collecting only those portions that contain the desired antigens. Because the complete cells are not used, infection is not possible. *Examples: newer whooping cough and typhoid vaccines.*

Biotechnology in Medicine

Code: RA 3

1. Describe briefly **how** each of the following types of vaccine are made and name an **example** of each:

   (a) Whole-agent vaccine: _____

   _____

   (b) Subunit vaccine: _____

   _____

   (c) Inactivated vaccine: _____

   _____

   (d) Attenuated vaccine: _____

   _____

   (e) Recombinant vaccine: _____

   _____

   (f) Toxoid vaccine: _____

   _____

   (g) Conjugated vaccine: _____

   _____

   (h) Acellular vaccine: _____

   _____

2. **Attenuated viruses** provide long term immunity to their recipients and generally do not require booster shots. Suggest a possible reason why attenuated viruses provide such effective long-term immunity when inactivated viruses do not:

   _____

   _____

3. Bearing in mind the structure of viruses, explain why **heat** cannot be used to kill viruses to make **inactivated vaccines**:

   _____

   _____

4. (a) Vaccines may now be produced using **DNA recombinant technology**. Describe an advantage of creating vaccines using these methods:

   _____

   (b) Draw a simple **diagram** to illustrate the use of the recombinant method to manufacture a vaccine:

Edible Vaccines

Although still a few years away, the development of edible vaccines produced by transgenic plants using **recombinant DNA technology** will overcome many of the problems faced when using traditional vaccines. Plants engineered to contain the vaccine can be grown locally, in the area where vaccination is required, overcoming the logistic and economic problems of transporting prepared vaccines over long distances. Most importantly, edible vaccines do not require syringes, saving money and eliminating the risk of infection from contaminated needles. One method (below) used to generate edible vaccines relies on the bacterium *Agrobacterium tumefaciens* to deliver the genes for viral or bacterial antigens into plant cells (e.g. potatoes).

Procedure for Making Edible Vaccines

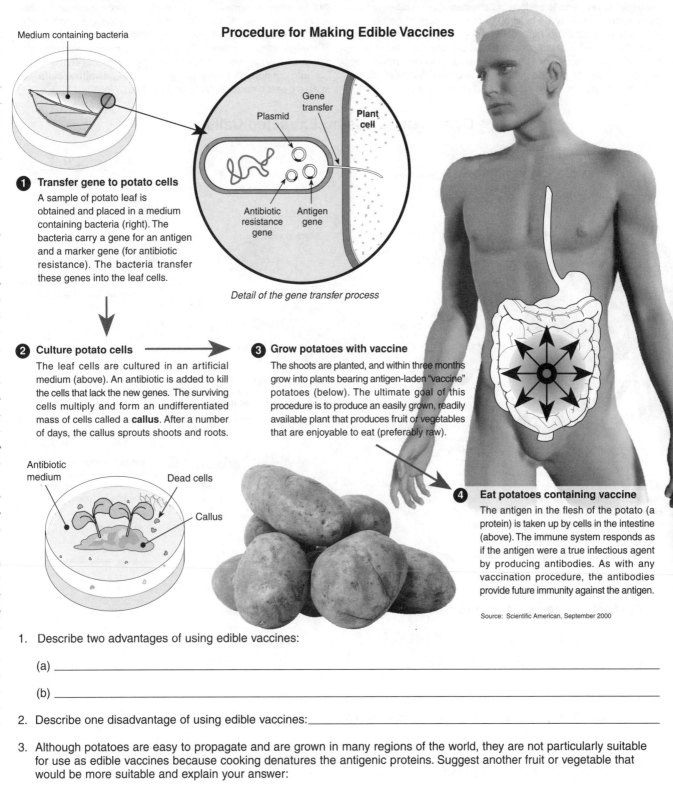

Medium containing bacteria

1 **Transfer gene to potato cells**

A sample of potato leaf is obtained and placed in a medium containing bacteria (right). The bacteria carry a gene for an antigen and a marker gene (for antibiotic resistance). The bacteria transfer these genes into the leaf cells.

Plasmid

Gene transfer

Plant cell

Antibiotic resistance gene

Antigen gene

Detail of the gene transfer process

2 **Culture potato cells**

The leaf cells are cultured in an artificial medium (above). An antibiotic is added to kill the cells that lack the new genes. The surviving cells multiply and form an undifferentiated mass of cells called a **callus**. After a number of days, the callus sprouts shoots and roots.

3 **Grow potatoes with vaccine**

The shoots are planted, and within three months grow into plants bearing antigen-laden "vaccine" potatoes (below). The ultimate goal of this procedure is to produce an easily grown, readily available plant that produces fruit or vegetables that are enjoyable to eat (preferably raw).

Antibiotic medium

Dead cells

Callus

4 **Eat potatoes containing vaccine**

The antigen in the flesh of the potato (a protein) is taken up by cells in the intestine (above). The immune system responds as if the antigen were a true infectious agent by producing antibodies. As with any vaccination procedure, the antibodies provide future immunity against the antigen.

Source: Scientific American, September 2000

Biotechnology in Medicine

1. Describe two advantages of using edible vaccines:

    (a) _____

    (b) _____

2. Describe one disadvantage of using edible vaccines: _____

3. Although potatoes are easy to propagate and are grown in many regions of the world, they are not particularly suitable for use as edible vaccines because cooking denatures the antigenic proteins. Suggest another fruit or vegetable that would be more suitable and explain your answer:

    _____

    _____

4. Explain why a gene for antibiotic resistance is added to the bacterium: _____

    _____

Gene Therapy

Gene therapy refers to the application of gene technology to correct or replace defective genes. It was first envisioned as a treatment, or even a cure, for genetic disorders, but it could also be used to treat a wide range of diseases, including those that resist conventional treatments. Gene therapy may operate by providing a correctly working version of a faulty gene or by adding a **novel gene** to perform a corrective role. In other cases, gene expression may be blocked in order to control cellular (or viral) activity. About two thirds of currently approved gene therapy procedures are targeting cancer, about one quarter aim to treat genetic disorders, such as cystic fibrosis, and the remainder are attempting to provide relief for infectious diseases. Gene therapy requires a **gene delivery system**; a way to transfer the gene to the patient's cells. This may be achieved using a infectious agent such as a virus; a technique called **transfection**. A promising development has been the recent approval for gene therapy to be used in treating tumours in cancer patients. Severe combined immune deficiency syndrome (SCIDS) has also shown improvement after gene therapy. Infants treated for this inherited, normally lethal condition have become healthy young adults (see below). Gene therapy involving **somatic cells** may be therapeutic, but the genetic changes are not inherited. The transfection of **stem cells**, rather than mature somatic cells, achieves a longer persistence of therapy in patients. In the future, the introduction of corrective genes into **germline cells** will enable genetic corrections to be inherited.

Gene Delivery Using Extracted Cells

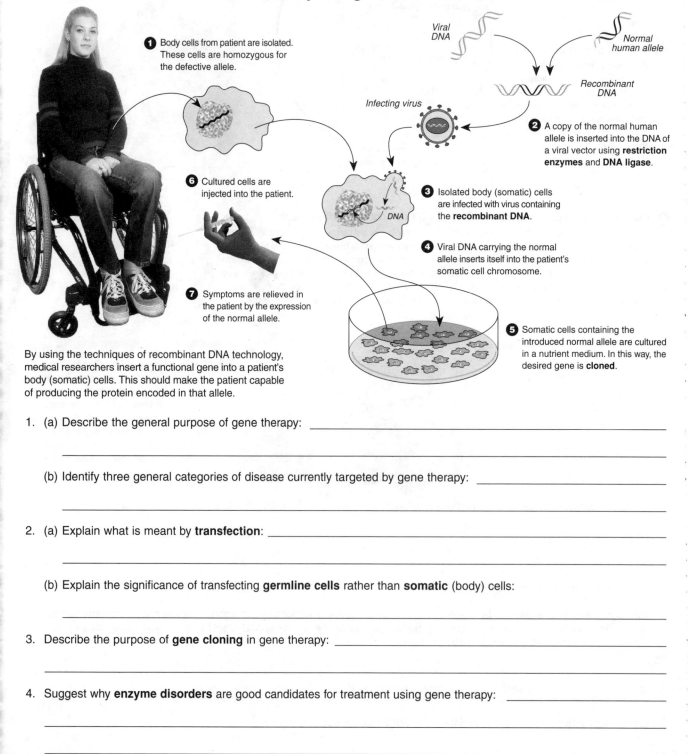

1. Body cells from patient are isolated. These cells are homozygous for the defective allele.

2. A copy of the normal human allele is inserted into the DNA of a viral vector using **restriction enzymes** and **DNA ligase**.

3. Isolated body (somatic) cells are infected with virus containing the **recombinant DNA**.

4. Viral DNA carrying the normal allele inserts itself into the patient's somatic cell chromosome.

5. Somatic cells containing the introduced normal allele are cultured in a nutrient medium. In this way, the desired gene is **cloned**.

6. Cultured cells are injected into the patient.

7. Symptoms are relieved in the patient by the expression of the normal allele.

Viral DNA

Normal human allele

Recombinant DNA

Infecting virus

DNA

By using the techniques of recombinant DNA technology, medical researchers insert a functional gene into a patient's body (somatic) cells. This should make the patient capable of producing the protein encoded in that allele.

1. (a) Describe the general purpose of gene therapy: _____

   _____

   (b) Identify three general categories of disease currently targeted by gene therapy: _____

   _____

2. (a) Explain what is meant by **transfection**: _____

   _____

   (b) Explain the significance of transfecting **germline cells** rather than **somatic** (body) cells:

   _____

3. Describe the purpose of **gene cloning** in gene therapy: _____

   _____

4. Suggest why **enzyme disorders** are good candidates for treatment using gene therapy: _____

   _____

   _____

Vectors for Gene Therapy

Gene therapy usually requires a **vector** (carrier) to introduce the DNA. The majority of approved clinical gene therapy protocols (63%) employ **retroviral vectors** to deliver the selected gene to the target cells, although there is considerable risk in using these vectors (below). Other widely used vectors include adenoviral vectors (16%), and liposomes (13%). The remaining 8% employ a variety of vector systems, the majority of which include injection of naked plasmid DNA.

Vectors That Can Be Used For Gene Therapy			
Retrovirus	**Adenovirus**	**Liposome**	**Naked DNA**
Insert size: 8000 bases	8000 bases	>20 000 bases	>20 000 bases
Integration: Yes	No	No	No
***In vivo* delivery:** Poor	High	Variable	Poor
Advantages • Integrate genes into the chromosomes of the human host cell. • Offers chance for long-term stability.	• Modified for gene therapy, they infect human cells and express the normal gene. • Most do not cause disease. • Have a large capacity to carry foreign genes.	• Liposomes seek out target cells using sugars in their membranes that are recognised by cell receptors. • Have no viral genes that may cause disease.	• Have no viral genes that may cause disease. • Expected to be useful for vaccination.
Disadvantages • Many infect only cells that are dividing. • Genes integrate randomly into chromosomes, so might disrupt useful genes in the host cell.	• Viruses may have poor survival due to attack by the host's immune system. • Genes may function only sporadically because they are not integrated into host cell's chromosome.	• Less efficient than viruses at transferring genes into cells, but recent work on using sugars to aid targeting have improved success rate.	• Unstable in most tissues of the body. • Inefficient at gene transfer.

In the table above, the following terms are defined as follows: **Naked DNA**: the genes are applied by ballistic injection (firing using a gene gun) or by regular hypodermic injection of plasmid DNA. **Insert size**: size of gene that can be inserted into the vector. **Integration**: whether or not the gene is integrated into the host DNA (chromosomes). ***In vivo* delivery**: ability to transfer a gene directly into a patient.

1. (a) Describe the features of viruses that make them well suited as **vectors** for gene therapy: _____

_____

_____

(b) Identify two problems with using viral vectors for gene therapy: _____

_____

_____

2. (a) Suggest why it may be beneficial for a (therapeutic) gene to integrate into the patient's chromosome: _____

_____

_____

(b) Explain why this has the potential to cause problems for the patient: _____

_____

3. (a) Suggest why naked DNA is likely to be unstable within a patient's tissues: _____

_____

(b) Suggest why enclosing the DNA within liposomes might provide greater stability: _____

_____

Code: RA 2

Gene Delivery Systems

The mapping of the human genome has improved the feasibility of gene therapy as a option for treating an increasingly wide range of diseases, but it remains technically difficult to deliver genes successfully to a patient. Even after a gene has been identified, cloned, and transferred to a patient, it must be expressed normally. To date, the success of gene therapy has been generally poor, and improvements have been short-lived or counteracted by adverse side effects. Inserted genes may reach only about 1% of target cells and those that reach their destination may work inefficiently and produce too little protein, too slowly to be of benefit. In addition, many patients react immunologically to the vectors used in gene transfer. Much of the current research is focussed on improving the efficiency of gene transfer and expression. One of the first gene therapy trials was for **cystic fibrosis** (CF). CF was an obvious candidate for gene therapy because, in most cases, the disease is caused by a single, known gene mutation. However, despite its early promise, gene therapy for this disease has been disappointing (below).

Gene Therapy as a Potential Treatment for Cystic Fibrosis (CF)

In cystic fibrosis, a gene mutation causes the body to produce an abnormally thick, sticky mucus that accumulates in the lungs and intestines. The identification and isolation of the CF gene in 1989 meant that scientists could look for ways in which to correct the genetic defect rather than just treating the symptoms using traditional therapies.

In trials, normal genes were isolated and inserted into patients using vectors such as **adenoviruses** and **liposomes**.

In order to prevent the progressive and ultimately lethal lung damage, the main target of CF gene therapy is the lung. The viral vector was piped directly into the lung, whereas the liposomes were inhaled in a spray formulation. The results of these trials were disappointing; on average, there was only a 25% correction, the effects were short lived, and the benefits were quickly reversed. Alarmingly, the adenovirus used in one of the trials led to the death of one patient.

Source: Cystic Fibrosis Trust, UK.

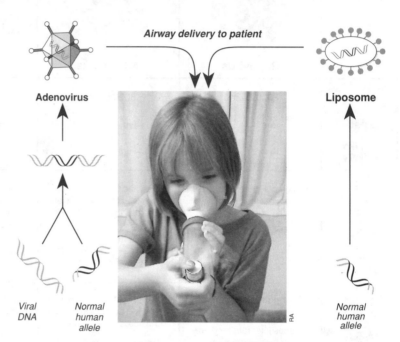

Airway delivery to patient

Adenovirus

Liposome

Viral DNA *Normal human allele*

Normal human allele

An **adenovirus** that normally causes colds is genetically modified to make it safe and to carry the normal (unmutated) CFTR ('cystic fibrosis') gene.

Liposomes are tiny fat globules. Normal CF genes are enclosed in liposomes, which fuse with plasma membranes and deliver the genes into the cells.

Gene Delivery Systems Used In Human Patients

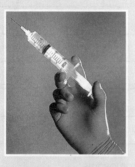

Hypodermic needle injection

- Injection of the vectors directly into the bloodstream or other organs of the patient. Vectors injected into the blood travel throughout the body and may be taken up by the target cells.
- Injections of plasmid DNA into thymus, skin, cardiac muscle and skeletal muscle have already proved successful in non-human trials (mice and primates).

Aerosol

- Aerosols and nebulisers offer an effective spread and efficient delivery of the vector to the site of certain target cells (especially in the respiratory tract).
- Used in trials of gene therapy for cystic fibrosis, but effective only on epithelial cells that can be reached by the aerosol.

Ballistic DNA injection is also called microprojectile gene transfer, the gene-gun, or particle bombardment method.

Ballistic DNA injection

- Plasmid DNA encoding the gene of interest is coated onto microbeads, and these are 'fired' at the target cells using gas pressure or a high voltage discharge.
- Used to transfer genes to a wide variety of cell lines *(ex vivo)* or directly into surgically exposed tissue *(in vivo)*.
- May be used in DNA-based vaccines to prevent infectious diseases or cancer.
- Allows delivery of precise DNA dosages. However, genes delivered by this method are expressed transiently and there is considerable cell damage at the centre of the discharge site.

An incubator for culturing cell lines (ex vivo).

©1999 University of Kansas Office of University Relations

Gene delivery to extracted cells and cell culture

- Target cells are isolated from tissue. Non-specific gene delivery is applied to the total cell population or as a microinjection of DNA into the nucleus of a single cell.
- Cells that have taken up the normal allele are cultured outside the body *(ex vivo)* and re-injected into the patient.
- The expression of the normal allele relieves symptoms of the disease.

1. A great deal of current research is being devoted to discovering a gene therapy solution to treat **cystic fibrosis** (CF):

   (a) Describe the symptoms of CF: _____

   _____

   _____

   (b) Explain why this genetic disease has been so eagerly targeted by gene therapy researchers: _____

   _____

   _____

   _____

   _____

   (c) Outline some of the problems so far encountered with gene therapy for CF: _____

   _____

   _____

   _____

   _____

   _____

2. Identify two vectors for introducing healthy CFTR genes into CF patients. For each vector, outline how it might be delivered to the patient and describe potential problems with its use:

   (a) Vector 1: _____

   Delivery: _____

   Problems: _____

   _____

   _____

   (b) Vector 2: _____

   Delivery: _____

   Problems: _____

   _____

   _____

3. Changes made to chromosomes as a result of gene therapy involving somatic cells are not inherited. Germ-line gene therapy has the potential to cure disease, but the risks and benefits are still not clear. For each of the points outlined below, evaluate the risk of germ-line gene therapy relative to somatic cell gene therapy and explain your answer:

   (a) Chance of interfering with an essential gene function: _____

   _____

   _____

   _____

   (b) Misuse of the therapy to selectively alter phenotype: _____

   _____

   _____

   _____

Genome Research

Investigating techniques and applications of DNA technology in gene research

DNA sequencing and profiling, DNA chips, genome analysis and genome projects.

Learning Objectives

☐ 1. Compile your own glossary from the **KEY WORDS** displayed in **bold type** in the learning objectives below.

Techniques in Genome Research *(pages 89-92)*

☐ 2. Describe the use of **PCR**, **radioactive labelling**, and **gel electrophoresis** in **DNA sequencing**. Distinguish between **manual** and **automated** sequencing. Outline how these techniques are used in **genome analysis**.

DNA profiling *(pages 95-98)*

☐ 3. Explain what is meant by **DNA profiling** and distinguish clearly between DNA profiling and sequencing.

☐ 4. Describe DNA profiling using PCR, including the role of the following:
   (a) **Microsatellites** in providing identifiable variation.
   (b) **PCR** in amplifying the microsatellites.
   (c) **Gel electrophoresis** in visualising the PCR products so that they can be compared.

☐ 5. Describe DNA profiling using a **Southern blot**. Explain the role of the following:
   (a) **Gel electrophoresis** to separate DNA fragments.
   (b) The **blot** to transfer the DNA fragments to a filter.
   (c) **Radioactively labelled probes** to localise and visualise the sought-after fragments.

☐ 6. Discuss how DNA profiling meets human needs and demands, for example:
   (a) As a tool in **forensic** analysis.
   (b) In establishing **pedigrees** in breeding animals.

   (c) As a tool in **diagnostic medicine**.

DNA microarrays *(pages 99-100)*

☐ 7. Describe the construction of a **DNA chip** (**microarray**), identifying the principles by which the chip operates. Discuss some of the current and potential applications of this relatively new technology in gene research.

Genome analysis *(pages 93-94, 101-105)*

☐ 8. Describe **genome analysis**, identifying the role of the techniques involved, including the use of restriction enzymes, DNA ligation, PCR, and gel electrophoresis.

☐ 9. Discuss the importance of automation to the feasibility of large-scale genome analyses and describe an appropriate example.

☐ 10. Describe the aim of the collaborative project known as the **Human Genome Project** (HGP). Describe possible applications of the information provided by the HGP, explaining how these will meet human needs/demands.

☐ 11. Identify areas of further development in genome analysis, e.g. determining when and where genes are expressed, and determining the role of the gene products (a field known as **proteomics**).

☐ 12. Describe some of the wider applications of DNA sequencing of both mitchondrial DNA (mtDNA) and nuclear DNA, for example:
   (a) Sequencing specific genes to look for variations between species and establish **phylogenies**.
   (b) Examining the genetic diversity of related species.
   (c) Examining dispersal or migration of related species.

See page 8 for additional details of these texts:

■ Chenn, P., 1997. **Microorganisms and Biotechnology** (John Murray), pp 123-129.
■ Freeland, P., 1999. **Microbes, Medicine and Commerce** (Hodder and Stoughton), chpt 6.
■ Jones, N., *et al.*, 2001. **The Essentials of Genetics** (John Murray), chpt 19.

See page 8 for details of publishers of periodicals:

■ **Sequence Me!** New Scientist, 21 Dec. 2002, pp. 44-47. *Which organisms have had their genomes sequenced and why? Which are next?*

■ **Bioinformatics** Biol. Sci. Rev., 15(3), February 2003, pp. 13-15 . *This account explores the bioinformation revolution. Bioinformatics is a branch of biology arising from the advancements in genome sequencing and development of the world wide web. A useful glossary of terms is provided.*

■ **Bioinformatics** Biol. Sci. Rev., 15(4) April 2003, pp. 2-6. *A follow up to the earlier account on the bioinformation revolution. This article looks at applications of bioinformatics in areas of basic biological and medical research.*

■ **Genes, the Genome, and Disease** New Scientist, 17 Feb. 2001, (Inside Science). *Understanding the human genome: producing genome maps, the role of introns in gene regulation, and the future of genomic research.*

■ **Beyond the Genome** New Scientist, 4 Nov. 2000, pp. 28-55. *A series of articles examining the future directions of genome analysis.*

■ **The Magic of Microarrays** Scientific American, Feb. 2002, pp. 34-41. *DNA chips (microarrays) and their use in identifying health and disease, along with implications for drug treatment.*

■ **Ready for Your Close-Up?** New Scientist, 20 July 2002, pp. 34-37. *A person's appearance can now be deduced from their DNA profile.*

See pages 4-5 for details of how to access **Bio Links** from our web site: **www.thebiozone.com** From Bio Links, access sites under the topics: **BIOTECHNOLOGY: > Biotechnology Processes:** • Basics of DNA fingerprinting • DNA fingerprinting in human health and society • DNA fingerprinting via Southern blotting ... *and others* > **Applications in Biotechnology** > **The Human Genome Project:** • A users guide to the human genome • Genome FAQs file ... *and others* > **Genome Projects:** • Genomes OnLine • Genome News Network ... *and others*

Presentation MEDIA to support this topic:

Genetics & Evolution CD-ROM:
• Set 9: Gene Technology

Manual DNA Sequencing

DNA sequencing techniques are used to determine the nucleotide (base) sequence of DNA. Two manual methods are in current use: the **Maxim-Gilbert** procedure and the most common method, the **Sanger** procedure (illustrated below). Both methods use a procedure called **electrophoresis**. The Sanger method is based on the premature termination of DNA synthesis resulting from the inclusion of specially modified nucleotides. DNA synthesis is initiated from a **primer** which is **radio-labelled** (contains a radioactive isotope that will appear on a photographic film called an **autoradiograph**). Four separate reactions are run, each containing a modified nucleotide mixed with its normal counterpart, as well as the three other normal nucleotides. When a modified nucleotide is added to the growing complementary DNA, synthesis stops. Each reaction yields a series of different sized fragments extending from the radioactive primer. The fragments from the four reactions are separated by electrophoresis and analysed by autoradiography to determine the DNA sequence.

The Sanger Method for DNA Sequencing

Four sequencing reactions

Using the same DNA sample to be sequenced (example used: **A C T G G T C T A G**), a separate sequencing reaction is carried out for each of the 4 bases: T, C, G, and A. In addition to the DNA sample, each reaction has normal (unaltered) copies of nucleotides: **T, C, G**, and **A**, plus a small quantity of one of the modified nucleotides:

Thymine reaction	Cytosine reaction	Guanine reaction	Adenine reaction
1% modified **T** is added to cause termination at random thymine sites	1% modified **C** is added to cause termination at random cytosine sites	1% modified **G** is added to cause termination at random guanine sites	1% modified **A** is added to cause termination at random adenine sites

Each test tube shows the variety of fragments produced by each reaction.

Radioactive primer attached to each fragment.

The nucleotides for a sequencing reaction for thymine includes **normal** nucleotides.

Modified thymine is added at random to each synthesising fragment which stops the DNA growing any longer.

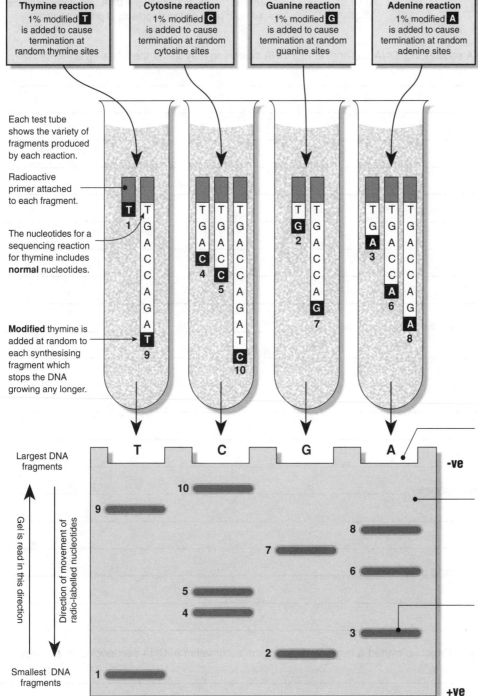

T C G A

A typical **autoradiograph** showing a DNA sequence. The unexposed film is laid in contact with the gel after it has run. Radioactivity from the clustered DNA fragments create the dark shadows (blobs). Each blob contains millions of fragments.

DNA samples: The four reactions containing DNA fragments are placed in separate wells at the top of the gel.

-ve

Electrophoresis gel: A jelly-like material that allows DNA fragments to move through it when an electric charge is applied. It is usually made of a material called *acrylamide*.

Radio-labelled DNA fragments: Attracted to the positive terminal, millions of DNA fragments of similar size and sequence move as a dark shadow down the gel. Larger pieces move more slowly and therefore do not travel as far.

Positive terminal: Attracts the fragments of DNA that are negatively charged.

+ve

Largest DNA fragments

Smallest DNA fragments

Gel is read in this direction

Direction of movement of radio-labelled nucleotides

Pharmacia (Aust) Pty Ltd

Genome Research

Code: RA 3

How Fragments Are Formed

1 The **sample DNA** being analysed is used repeatedly as a *template* to produce complementary fragments of different lengths.

'Unknown' DNA sequence

These numbers are used to designate what direction the DNA is being read; synthesis is always started at the 3' end of the template.

3' A C T G G T C T A G 5'

5' 3' T G A C C A G

Synthesises in this direction

2 **Radioactive primer** is attached to each DNA fragment (this is what causes the blob on the film).

3 **Complementary DNA** strands of varying lengths will form opposite the sequence to be analysed.

4 Synthesis of this particular fragment stops at the 7th base because a modified guanine was added which stops further growth of the complementary DNA strand.

Creating the fragments

How long each fragment will be depends on what position one of the *chemically altered nucleotides* is incorporated into the sequence:

T Thymine
C Cytosine
G Guanine
A Adenine

Chemically altered so that they prevent further synthesis of the complementary DNA

What must be realised is that the DNA sample being analysed consists of many millions of individual molecules, each being used as a template to make fragments. Each template molecule itself will produce thousands of complementary DNA fragments of varying lengths. In the sample DNA above, the guanine reaction can produce two fragments of different lengths.

1. Briefly describe how PCR, DNA sequencing, DNA profiling, and/or DNA screening may assist the following areas of study:

(a) Forensic science: _____

_____

_____

(b) Legal disputes: _____

_____

_____

(c) Medical applications: _____

_____

_____

(d) Investigations into evolutionary relationships and taxonomy: _____

_____

_____

(e) Archaeology and anthropology: _____

_____

_____

(f) Conservation of endangered species: _____

_____

_____

(g) Management of livestock breeding programmes: _____

_____

_____

2. Explain why the Human Genome Project provided a large stimulus for the automation of DNA sequencing technology:

_____

_____

Automated DNA Sequencing

The process of DNA sequencing can be automated using **gel electrophoresis** machines that can sequence up to 600 bases at a time. Automation improves the speed at which samples can be sequenced and has made large scale sequencing projects (such as the **Human Genome Project**) possible. Instead of using radio-labelled DNA fragments, automated sequencing uses nucleotides labelled with **fluorescent dyes**; a different colour is used for each of the four types of bases. Another advantage is that the entire base sequence for a sample can be determined from a single lane on the gel (not four lanes as with the manual method). Computer software automatically interprets the data from the gel and produces a base sequence.

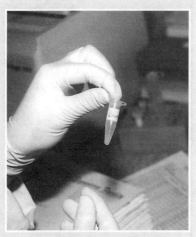

1. DNA sample arrives

Purified DNA samples may contain linear DNA or plasmids. The sample should contain about 1×10^{11} DNA molecules. The sample is checked to ensure that there is enough DNA present in the sample to work with.

2. Primer and reaction mix added

A **DNA primer** is added to the sample which provides a starting sequence for synthesis. Also added is the **sequencing reaction mix** containing the *polymerase enzyme* and free nucleotides, some which are labelled with dye.

All photos are RA (unless indicated otherwise)

3. Create dye-labelled fragments

A **PCR** machine creates fragments of DNA complementary to the original template DNA. Each fragment is tagged with a fluorescent dye-labelled nucleotide. Running for 25 cycles, it creates 25×10^{11} single-stranded DNA molecules.

4. Centrifuge to create DNA pellet

The sample is chemically precipitated and centrifuged to settle the DNA fragments as a solid pellet at the bottom of the tube. Unused nucleotides, still in the liquid, are discarded.

5. DNA pellet washed, buffer added

The pellet is washed with ethanol, dried, and a gel loading buffer is added. All that remains now is single stranded DNA with one dye-labelled nucleotide at the end of each molecule.

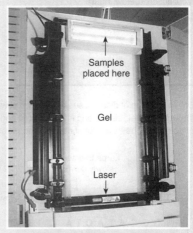

Samples placed here

Gel

Laser

6. Acrylamide gel is loaded

The DNA sequencer is prepared by placing the gel (sandwiched between two sheets of glass) into position. A 36 channel 'comb' for receiving the samples is placed at the top of the gel.

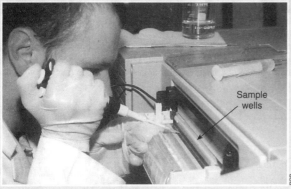

Sample wells

7. Loading DNA samples onto gel

Different samples can be placed in each of the 36 wells (funnel shaped receptacles) above the gel. A control DNA sample of known sequence is applied to the first lane of the sequencer. If there are problems with the control sequence then results for all other lanes are considered invalid.

8. Running the DNA sequencer

Powerful computer software controls the activity of the DNA sequencer. The gel is left to run for up to 10 hours. During this time an argon laser is constantly scanning across the bottom of the gel to detect the passing of dye-labelled nucleotides attached to DNA fragments.

Genome Research

How a DNA Sequencer Operates

The gel is loaded following preparation of the samples and the gel (see steps 1-7 opposite and box, right).

Comb with 36 lanes into which different samples can be placed.

DNA fragments with dye-labelled nucleotides move down the gel over a period of 10 hours.

The smallest fragments move fastest down the gel and reach the argon laser first. Larger fragments arrive later.

DNA fragments separate into bands (see box below).

Argon laser excites fluorescent dye labels on nucleotides.

Lenses collect the emitted light and focus it into a spectro-graph. An attached digital camera detects the light. See 'data collection' (below, right).

Negative terminal repels DNA fragments

Acrylamide gel

2400 volts
50 mA

Positive terminal attracts DNA fragments

Creating the dye labelled fragments
for gel electrophoresis is outlined in step 3, opposite. Key ingredients are:

(a) Original DNA template (the sample)

A C C G T A T G A T T C

(b) Many normal unlabelled nucleotides:

A   T   G   C

(c) Terminal nucleotides labelled with fluorescent dye (a different colour for each of the 4 bases). The structure of the nucleotides is altered so they act as terminators to stop further synthesis of the strand:

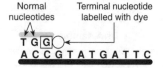

Two examples of synthesised DNA fragments are shown below. One is relatively short, the other is longer:

Normal nucleotides   Terminal nucleotide labelled with dye

T G G ○

A C C G T A T G A T T C

T G G C A T A C T ●

A C C G T A T G A T T C

Data collection: The data from the digital camera are collected by computer software. The first of 23 samples is highlighted below in lane 1 with base sequences appearing on the far left.

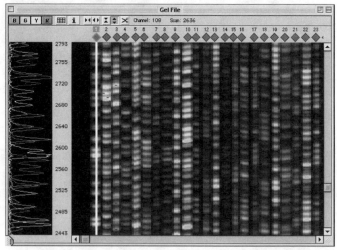

Data analysis: The data can be saved as a computer file which can then be analysed by other computer software. Such software can provide a printout of the base sequence as well as carry out comparisons with other DNA sequences (such as when looking for mutations).

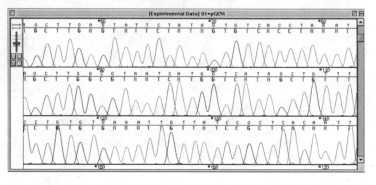

DNA fragments of different sizes are drawn down through the gel, separating into distinct bands of colour as they are illuminated by the laser:

Large fragments travel slowly down the gel

T G G C A T A C T A A G ○ Yellow

T G G C A T A C T A A ● Green

T G G C A T A C T A ● Green

T G G C A T A C T ● Red

T G G C A T A C ● Blue

T G G C A T A ● Green

T G G C A T ● Red

T G G C A ● Green

T G G C ● Blue

T G G ○ Yellow

T G ○ Yellow

T ● Red

Small fragments travel quickly down the gel

Laser scans across the gel to detect the passing of each coloured dye

Genome Analysis

Genome analysis involves determining the exact order of all of the millions of bases making up the DNA of an organism's **genome**. Genome analysis must also identify all the genes present, their correct and exact location in the base sequence, and the regions of DNA that control the activity of the genes. Chromosomes range in size from 50 million to 250 million bases; too large to handle for high resolution mapping and sequencing. They must be broken down into much shorter pieces, cloned, and sequenced. It is important to be able to assemble all of the sequenced fragments into a complete, continuous sequence for each chromosome. This is achieved by mapping known **genetic** **markers** at regular intervals along each chromosome. When DNA fragments are sequenced, the presence of DNA markers enables them to be correctly positioned in the overall sequence. A wide variety of applications are currently or potentially available for genome analysis, from the treatment and diagnosis of disease to ecological studies of diversity and phylogeny. Note that a small proportion of an organism's DNA occurs outside the nucleus, in the mitochondria, and is called the **mitochondrial genome**. Mitochondrial DNA (mtDNA) is often targeted in studies of phylogeny because it is highly **conserved** (it codes for vital functions and changes very little over evolutionary time).

Mapping and Sequencing the Genome

1. Chromosome cut into large fragments:

A human chromosome, consisting of 50-280 million base-pairs, is cut randomly into large fragments with **restriction enzymes**. Each fragment is 150 000 - 1 million base pairs long.

2. Create a clone library:

Each large fragment is inserted into a separate vector (yeast or bacterial plasmid) using DNA **ligation**. The plasmids are then cloned in cells to produce many copies of the fragments; known as a **clone library** (each type of DNA fragment resides in a separate culture).

3. Map fragment with DNA markers:

Each of the fragments are then mapped using **PCR** and **gel electrophoresis** to determine the position of **DNA markers** on each fragment.

4. Create a low resolution map of a chromosome:

Overlaps between the large fragments can be determined and a low resolution map of the chromosome can be built up. In reality, there would be many hundreds of large fragments created by the cutting up of a single chromosome (only four are shown here).

5. Each large fragment is cut into smaller pieces:

A large fragment is cut into smaller pieces (1500 - 5000 base pairs) with **restriction enzymes**. These smaller fragments are inserted into vectors using DNA **ligation** techniques. These vectors are then cloned to make copies; a **sub-clone library**.

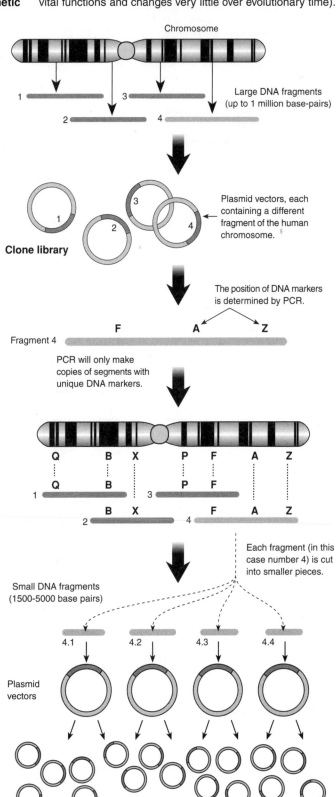

Chromosome

Large DNA fragments (up to 1 million base-pairs)

Clone library

Plasmid vectors, each containing a different fragment of the human chromosome.

The position of DNA markers is determined by PCR.

Fragment 4

PCR will only make copies of segments with unique DNA markers.

Each fragment (in this case number 4) is cut into smaller pieces.

Small DNA fragments (1500-5000 base pairs)

Plasmid vectors

Sub-clone library

Genome Research

Code: RA 2

6 Sequence fragments:

The small fragments are then sequenced using **gel electrophoresis** to find the exact order of the bases. Note: the examples on the right show only 15 base-pairs in each small fragment. In reality, they would be 1500 to 5000 base pairs in length.

7 Overlapping sequences are assembled:

Overlapping sequences are assembled together using a computer to work out the sequence of the large fragment.

Steps 5-7 are repeated for all large fragments until the entire chromosome is sequenced.

8 Assemble sequenced fragments on chromosome:

The sequences of the large fragments are then assembled on the chromosome map to make a complete chromosome sequence.

Base sequence

Small fragments

4.1	AGCCTACGTATATTC
4.2	TATATTCTCAGGACC
4.3	CTCAGGACCAATACG
4.4	AATACGTAGGATTCC

4.1 AGCCTACGTATATTC
4.2   TATATTCTCAGGACC
4.3   CTCAGGACCAATACG
4.4   AATACGTAGGATTCC

AGCCTACGTATATTCTCAGGACCAATACGTAGGATTCC

Large fragment 4

Chromosome

1. Explain how the following two main components of genome analysis contribute to the overall process:

   (a) Genome **mapping**: _____

   _____

   (b) Genome **sequencing**: _____

   _____

2. Explain the difference between a **clone library** and a **sub-clone library**, identifying their role in genome analysis:

   _____

   _____

   _____

   _____

   _____

3. Describe the steps in the genome analysis process where the following techniques are used:

   (a) Restriction enzymes: _____

   _____

   (b) Ligation: _____

   _____

   (c) Polymerase Chain Reaction (PCR): _____

   _____

   (d) Gel electrophoresis: _____

   _____

4. Explain the role that DNA markers play in genome analysis: _____

   _____

   _____

DNA Profiling Using PCR

In chromosomes, some of the DNA contains simple, repetitive sequences. These *noncoding* nucleotide sequences repeat themselves over and over again and are found scattered throughout the genome. Some repeating sequences are short (2-6 base pairs) called **microsatellites** or **short tandem repeats** (STRs) and can repeat up to 100 times. The human genome has numerous different microsatellites. Equivalent sequences in different people vary considerably in the numbers of the repeating unit. This phenomenon has been used to develop **DNA profiling** which identifies the natural variations found in every person's DNA. Identifying such differences in the DNA

of individuals is a useful tool for forensic investigations. Every country has its own laboratory approved for forensic DNA testing. The lab is responsible for providing a national DNA database of samples from convicted criminals, suspects, and crime scenes. It targets 10-13 core STR sites; enough to guarantee that the odds of someone else sharing the same result are extremely unlikely (about one in a billion, i.e. a thousand million). DNA profiling can also be used for investigating genetic relatedness (e.g. paternity cases, checking the pedigrees of bloodstock), or for searching for the presence of a particular gene (e.g. genetic screening for diseases).

Microsatellites (Short Tandem Repeats)

Microsatellites consist of a variable number of tandem repeats of a 2 to 6 base pair sequence. In the example below it is a two base sequence (CA) that is repeated.

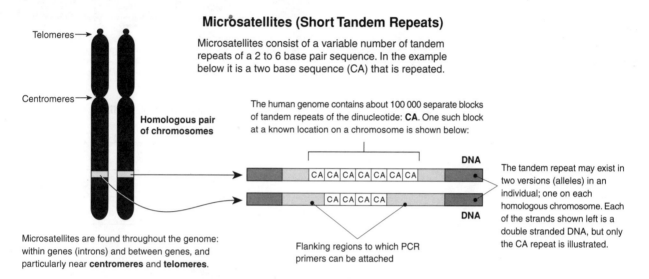

The human genome contains about 100 000 separate blocks of tandem repeats of the dinucleotide: **CA**. One such block at a known location on a chromosome is shown below:

Telomeres

Centromeres

Homologous pair of chromosomes

The tandem repeat may exist in two versions (alleles) in an individual; one on each homologous chromosome. Each of the strands shown left is a double stranded DNA, but only the CA repeat is illustrated.

Microsatellites are found throughout the genome: within genes (introns) and between genes, and particularly near **centromeres** and **telomeres**.

Flanking regions to which PCR primers can be attached

How short tandem repeats are used in DNA profiling

This diagram shows how three people can have quite different microsatellite arrangements at the same point (locus) in their DNA. Each will produce a different DNA profile using gel electrophoresis:

1 **Extract DNA from sample**

A sample collected from the tissue of a living or dead organism is treated with chemicals and enzymes to extract the DNA, which is separated and purified.

2 **Amplify microsatellite using PCR**

Specific primers (arrowed) that attach to the flanking regions (light grey) either side of the microsatellite are used to make large quantities of the microsatellite and flanking regions sequence only (no other part of the DNA is amplified/replicated).

3 **Visualise fragments on a gel**

The fragments are separated by length, using **gel electrophoresis**. DNA, which is negatively charged, moves toward the positive terminal. The smaller fragments travel faster than larger ones.

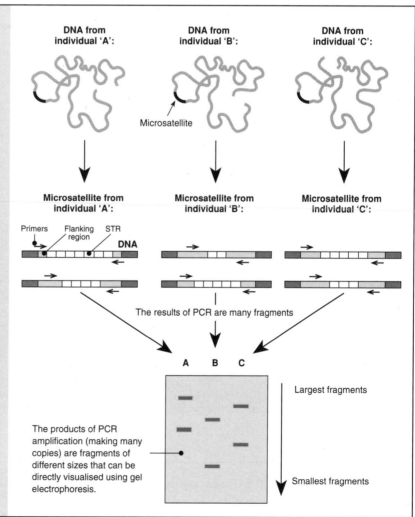

The products of PCR amplification (making many copies) are fragments of different sizes that can be directly visualised using gel electrophoresis.

Genome Research

Code: A 3

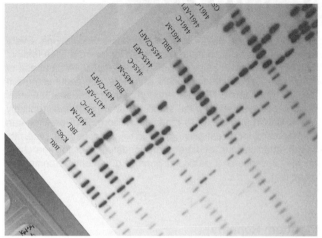
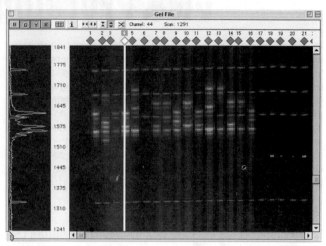

The photo above shows a film output from a DNA profiling procedure. Those lanes with many regular bands are used for calibration; they contain DNA fragment sizes of known length. These calibration lanes can be used to determine the length of fragments in the unknown samples.

DNA profiling can be automated in the same way as DNA sequencing. Powerful computer software is able to display the results of many samples that are run at the same time. In the photo above, the sample in lane 4 has been selected and displays fragments of different length on the left of the screen.

1. Describe the properties of **short tandem repeats** that are important to the application of **DNA profiling** technology:

_____

_____

_____

_____

_____

2. Explain the role of each of the following techniques in the process of DNA profiling:

(a) Gel electrophoresis: _____

_____

_____

(b) PCR: _____

_____

_____

3. Describe the three main steps in DNA profiling using PCR:

(a) _____

_____

_____

(b) _____

_____

_____

(c) _____

_____

_____

_____

4. Explain why as many as 10 STR sites are used to gain a DNA profile for forensic evidence: _____

_____

DNA Profiling Using Probes

Although DNA profiling using PCR is becoming increasingly the dominant procedure, the older technology of using DNA probes is still in use. This method uses another type of repeat sequence to that used in profiling with PCR. The repeat sequences are called **minisatellites** or **variable number tandem repeats** (VNTRs), and comprise longer repeating units (a few tens of nucleotides long). Equivalent sequences in different people have the same core sequence of 10-15 bases (to which a DNA **probe** is attached), but thereafter the patterns vary considerably in length from one person to another. This phenomenon has been used to develop a DNA profiling procedure called the Southern blot (illustrated below). In humans, the chance that two people will have an identical DNA profile is less than one in a billion, making DNA profiling a useful tool for forensic investigations.

Southern Blotting Method

Gene of interest

❶ Extract DNA from sample
A sample of tissue from a living or dead organism is treated with chemicals and enzymes to extract the DNA, which is separated and purified.

❷ Cut up DNA
Using **restriction enzymes**, the DNA is cut up into thousands of fragments of all different sizes.

❸ Separate fragments
The fragments are separated by length, using **gel electrophoresis**. DNA, which is negatively charged, moves toward the positive terminal. The shorter fragments travel faster and further than longer ones.

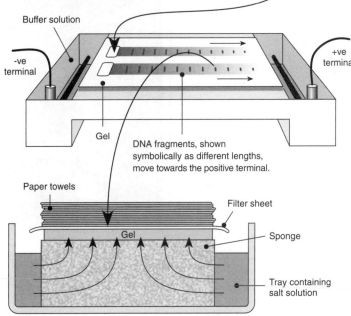

Buffer solution

-ve terminal

+ve terminal

Gel

DNA fragments, shown symbolically as different lengths, move towards the positive terminal.

Paper towels

Filter sheet

Gel

Sponge

Tray containing salt solution

❹ Transfer DNA fragments to filter sheet
DNA molecules are split into single strands using alkaline chemicals. The DNA is transferred onto a nitrocellulose filter sheet by pressing it against the gel. The salt solution passes through the gel, carrying the DNA fragments onto the surface of the filter sheet. This is the blot.

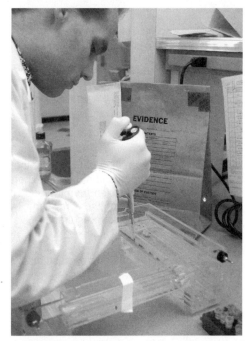

A technician carrying out a DNA profiling test of samples taken from the scene of a crime. Such tests are admissible in a court of law as forensic evidence.

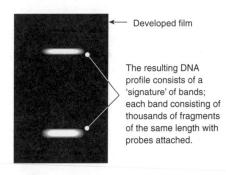

Developed film

The resulting DNA profile consists of a 'signature' of bands; each band consisting of thousands of fragments of the same length with probes attached.

❼ Create autoradiograph
When using radioactive probes, the filter sheet is exposed to X-ray film. The radioactive probes attached to the sorted fragments show up as dark bands on the film. The spacing of these bands is the **DNA profile**, which is used as evidence.

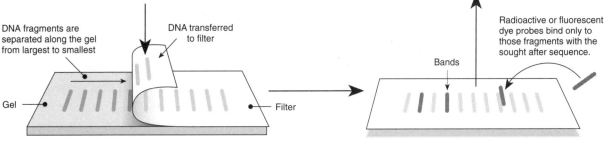

DNA fragments are separated along the gel from largest to smallest

DNA transferred to filter

Gel

Filter

Bands

Radioactive or fluorescent dye probes bind only to those fragments with the sought after sequence.

❺ Remove filter sheet
The gel with filter sheet still attached is removed and separated. The DNA fragments that have now moved to the filter sheet are in exactly the same position as on the gel.

❻ Attach radioactively labelled probes
The filter sheet is immersed in a bath with **radioactive probes** (synthetic complementary DNA). Many thousands of these segments bind to the sample DNA fragments where they are localised as bands.

Genome Research

How DNA probes may be used

Artificially constructed DNA probes work by binding to a specific sequence on DNA that is of interest to the investigator. Gene probes may be used to search for:

- The presence of a specific allele of a gene (e.g. cystic fibrosis gene).

- The approximate location of a gene on a chromosome (i.e. which chromosome and what position on its *p* or *q* arm it binds to).

- The 'genetic fingerprint' of a person to tell them apart from others (e.g. paternity testing, forensic identification of suspects).

How a DNA probe works

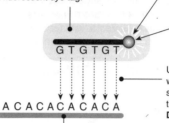

A **DNA probe** is a small fragment of nucleic acid (either cloned or artificially synthesised), that is labelled with an *enzyme*, a *radioactive* tag, or a *fluorescent dye* tag.

Fluorescent dye tag: Shows up as fluorescent bands when gel is exposed to ultraviolet light source.

or

Radioactive tag: Shows up as a dark band when the gel is exposed to photographic film.

G T G T G T

A C A C A C A C A C A

Under appropriate conditions, the probe will bind to a complementary DNA sequence by base pairing, identifying the presence and location of the **target DNA** sequence for further analysis.

Target DNA strand (such as a tandem repeat) with a complementary sequence that is being searched for by the probe.

---

1. The DNA profile on the right is a hypothetical example of a forensic result where the victim was raped and murdered. There were three suspects in the case. A semen sample was taken from the body of the victim and this was used as the evidence (see arrow on the X-ray film). Two probes were used in this investigation. The three suspects were required to give blood samples and a sample was also taken from the victim.

   (a) Identify which of the three suspects was probably the killer: _____

   (b) Explain with what degree of certainty do you give this verdict:

   _____

   _____

   (c) Explain why a sample from the **victim** was also taken and analysed:

   _____

   _____

2. Explain why DNA profiling is a more useful diagnostic tool for **forensic** analysis than simply using **blood types**:

   _____

   _____

   _____

   _____

   > FORENSICS GEL #: 15423   RUN DATE:
   > EXP TIME: PROBE:
   >
   > Suspect 1 Suspect 2 Suspect 3 Evidence Victim

3. In some well-known criminal trials in recent years (e.g. the trial of 'O.J. Simpson' for the murder of his wife, USA, 1995) the prosecution cases relied heavily on DNA evidence. Despite providing a DNA profile of the accused that clearly implicated them in the crime, the evidence was successfully challenged by defence counsel on technical grounds (concerning what is called the '**chain of evidence**'). Explain why such DNA evidence has failed to gain a prosecution:

   _____

   _____

   _____

4. Forensic applications of DNA profiling are well known. Briefly describe two other applications of DNA profiling:

   (a) _____

   _____

   (b) _____

   _____

DNA Chips

Microarrays (DNA chips or gene chips) are relatively recent tools in gene research. Their development a decade ago built on earlier DNA probe technology and provided a tool to quickly compare the (known) DNA on a chip with (unknown) DNA to determine which genes were present in a sample or to determine the code of an unsequenced string of DNA. Microarrays have also provided a tool which, increasingly, is being used to investigate the activity level (the expression) of those genes. Microarrays rely on **nucleic acid hybridisation**, in which a known DNA fragment is used as a **probe** to find complementary sequences. In a microarray, DNA fragments, corresponding to known genes, are fixed to a solid support in an orderly pattern, usually as a series of dots. The fragments are tested for hybridisation with samples of labelled cDNA molecules. Computer analysis then reveals which genes are active in different tissues, in different stages of development, or in tissues in different states of health.

What is a DNA Chip?

A **microarray** (DNA chip) consists of DNA probes fixed to a small solid support such as a glass slide or a nylon filter. Each spot on the microarray has thousands to millions of copies of a different **DNA probe**. The probes are single stranded DNA molecules, each representing a gene.

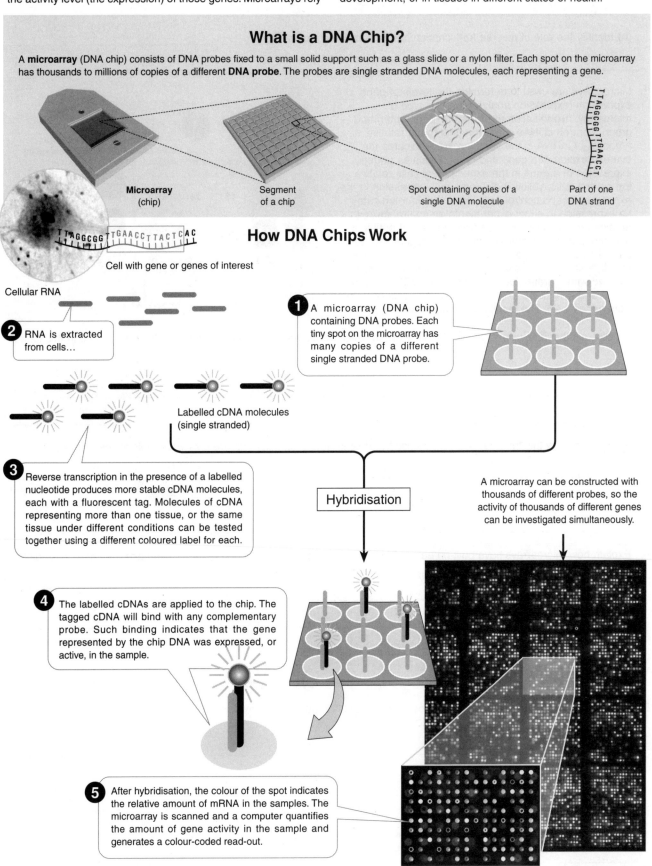

Microarray (chip)

Segment of a chip

Spot containing copies of a single DNA molecule

Part of one DNA strand

Cell with gene or genes of interest

How DNA Chips Work

Cellular RNA

2 RNA is extracted from cells...

1 A microarray (DNA chip) containing DNA probes. Each tiny spot on the microarray has many copies of a different single stranded DNA probe.

Labelled cDNA molecules (single stranded)

3 Reverse transcription in the presence of a labelled nucleotide produces more stable cDNA molecules, each with a fluorescent tag. Molecules of cDNA representing more than one tissue, or the same tissue under different conditions can be tested together using a different coloured label for each.

Hybridisation

A microarray can be constructed with thousands of different probes, so the activity of thousands of different genes can be investigated simultaneously.

4 The labelled cDNAs are applied to the chip. The tagged cDNA will bind with any complementary probe. Such binding indicates that the gene represented by the chip DNA was expressed, or active, in the sample.

5 After hybridisation, the colour of the spot indicates the relative amount of mRNA in the samples. The microarray is scanned and a computer quantifies the amount of gene activity in the sample and generates a colour-coded read-out.

Genome Research

1. Describe one purpose of microarrays: _____

   _____

   _____

2. (a) Identify the basic principle by which microarrays work: _____

   _____

   _____

   (b) Identify the role of reverse transcription in microarray technology: _____

   _____

3. Microarrays are used to determine the levels of gene expression (expression analysis). In one type of microarray, hybridisation of the red (experimental) and green (control) cDNAs is proportional to the relative amounts of mRNA in the samples. Red indicates the overexpression of a gene and green indicates under-expression of a gene in the experimental cells relative the control cells, yellow indicates equal expression in the experimental and control cells, and no colour indicates no expression in either experimental or control cells. In an experiment, cDNA derived from a strain of antibiotic resistant bacteria (experimental cells) was labelled with a red fluorescent tag and cDNA derived from a a non-resistant strain of the same bacterium (control cells) was labelled with a green fluorescent tag. The cDNAs were mixed and hybridised to a chip containing spots of DNA from genes 1-25. The results are shown on the right.

   (a) Discuss the conclusions you could make about which genes might be implicated in antibiotic resistance in this case:

   _____

   _____

   _____

   (b) Suggest how this information could be used to design new antibiotics that are less vulnerable to resistance:

   _____

   _____

   _____

4. Explain how microarrays have built on earlier DNA probe technology and describe the advantages they offer in studies of gene expression:

   _____

   _____

   _____

   _____

5. Microarrays are frequently used in diagnostic medicine to compare gene expression in cancerous and non-cancerous tissue. Suggest how this information could be used:

   _____

   _____

   _____

   _____

   _____

Investigating Genetic Biodiversity

PCR and **DNA sequencing** can be used in the assessment of **genetic biodiversity**. From a conservation point of view, large amounts of genetic variation within a species may be indicative of a greater ability to adapt to environmental change (e.g. changes in climate). The amount of variation between populations of a species is of particular interest. Sometimes the genetic variation found between populations is enough to warrant separating them into two or more '**morphologically cryptic**' species (containing populations that are identical in appearance, but different genetically). **Springtails** are abundant arthropods, closely related to insects, which live in soil throughout the world. One particular species, *Gomphiocephalus hodgsoni*, is the largest year-round inhabitant of the Antarctic continent. It is

being studied in an area of Antarctica known as the Dry Valleys, particularly in Taylor Valley. This region is largely ice-free, and the springtails survive in moist habitats such as at the edges of lakes and glacial streams. Springtails collected throughout Taylor Valley appear to be morphologically identical. However, after DNA analysis of a gene from springtail **mitochondrial DNA**, significant genetic biodiversity has been found between populations. This may indicate the presence of more than one species. As climate change and the presence of humans affect the habitat of Taylor Valley over time, it is important to understand and monitor the genetic structure of the springtail populations in order to ensure that biodiversity is conserved.

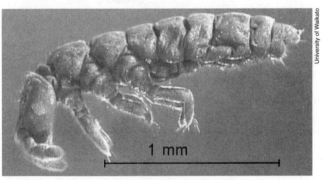

The **springtail** *Gomphiocephalus hodgsoni* (above) is a small arthropod, just over 1 mm long. Liam Nolan investigated the genetic relatedness of populations in and around Taylor Valley in Antarctica.

Taylor Valley, one of the Dry Valleys in Antarctica, is clear of snow much of the year. The ephemeral stream is ideal springtail habitat.

The Process of DNA Analysis of Two Springtails (A and B) is illustrated below:

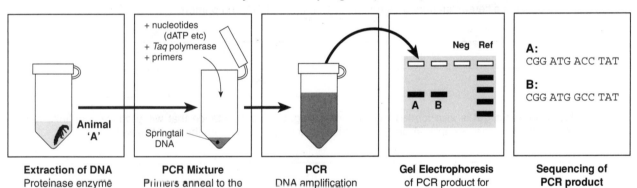

Extraction of DNA
Proteinase enzyme dissolves the tissues of the springtail to release DNA

PCR Mixture
Primers anneal to the start and end of the gene in the mitochondrial DNA

PCR
DNA amplification 92°C, 45°C, 72°C 45 cycles

Gel Electrophoresis
of PCR product for both animal 'A' and 'B'

Sequencing of PCR product

A:
CGG ATG ACC TAT

B:
CGG ATG GCC TAT

Source: Many thanks to Liam Nolan, teacher at Tauranga Girls' College, for supplying the information for these pages. Liam studied with the **Centre for Biodiversity and Ecology Research** (University of Waikato, Hamilton, New Zealand), whilst the recipient of a study award from the NZ Ministry of Education.

Conditions in Antarctica are harsh, even at the best of times. Members of the research group shared a tent at their camp in Taylor Valley, set aside as a field laboratory. Despite overnight temperatures well below freezing, the tent often became very hot during the day as the mid-summer sun heated it for most of the 24 hour cycle.

Genome Research

Scientific expeditions into the field in Antarctica are fraught with logistical problems. Apart from making sure that sophisticated scientific equipment functions properly in freezing temperatures, just getting the equipment from Scott Base to the field station is difficult, requiring the use of helicopters.

Scott Base is the centre for research by New Zealand scientists. They work mostly during the summer months, when there is perpetual daylight. There are facilities for carrying out some lab work, as well as recreational facilities for the expedition members.

1. Explain why a **proteinase** enzyme is helpful in the extraction of DNA from springtails:

2. (a) Describe the function of *Taq* polymerase in **PCR**:

   (b) Explain why nucleotides are added to the PCR mixture:

   (c) Explain the effect of different temperatures (used in PCR) on the DNA and primers:

3. (a) The **electrophoresis gel** is also loaded with a known '**negative**'; a substance that will produce a definite negative result, for comparison with samples A and B. Describe what would be put into the negative well:

   (b) A **reference**, which contains a mixture of DNA segments of known length, is also loaded onto the gel. Explain why such fragments are added into the reference well:

4. (a) The given DNA sequences (on the previous page) are taken from two different individuals. Describe the kind of mutation observed:

   (b) Mutations are most frequently found at the third base of a codon. Discuss the significance of this mutation in the springtails' DNA sequence:

The Human Genome Project

The **Human Genome Project** (HGP) is a publicly funded venture involving many different organisations throughout the world. In 1998, Celera Genomics in the USA began a competing project, as a commercial venture, in a race to be the first to determine the human genome sequence. In 2000, both organisations reached the first draft stage, and the entire genome is now available as a high quality (**Gold Standard**) sequence. In addition to determining the order of bases in the human genome, genes are being identified, sequenced, and mapped (their specific chromosomal location identified). The next challenge is to assign functions to the identified genes. By identifying and studying the protein products of genes (a field known as **proteomics**), scientists can develop a better understanding of genetic disorders. Long term benefits of the HGP are both medical and non-medical (see over page). Many biotechnology companies have taken out patents on gene sequences. This practice is controversial because it restricts the use of the sequence information to the patent holders. Other genome sequencing projects have arisen as a result of the initiative to sequence the human one. A controversial project to map the differences between racial and ethnic groups is the **Human Genome Diversity Project** (HGDP). It aims to understand the degree of diversity amongst individuals in the human species. It is still in its planning stages, seeking the best way to achieve its goals.

Gene Mapping

This process involves determining the precise position of a gene on a chromosome. Once the position is known, it can be shown on a diagram.

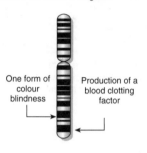

One form of colour blindness

Production of a blood clotting factor

X chromosome

Equipment used for DNA Sequencing

Banks of PCR machines prepare DNA for the sequencing gel stage. The DNA is amplified and chemically tagged (to make the DNA fluoresce and enable visualisation on a gel).

Banks of DNA sequencing gels and powerful computers are used to determine the base order in DNA.

Count of Mapped Genes

The length and number of mapped genes to date for each chromosome are tabulated below. The entire human genome contains approximately 20 000-25 000 genes.

Chromosome	Length (Mb)	No. of Mapped Genes
1	263	1871
2	255	1113
3	214	964
4	203	613
5	194	782
6	183	1216
7	171	995
8	155	589
9	145	802
10	144	872
11	144	1162
12	143	892
13	114	290
14	109	1013
15	106	509
16	98	656
17	92	1034
18	85	302
19	67	1128
20	72	599
21	50	386
22	56	501
X	164	1020
Y	59	122
Total:		**19 431**

As at: 19 March 2006 For an update see:
**http://gdbwww.gdb.org/gdbreports/
CountGeneByChromosome.html**

Composition of the Genome

About 97% of the genome does not code for protein and its function was largely unknown. Recent genomic analyses have revealed that some this DNA (the intronic DNA) codes for functional RNA molecules with important regulatory roles. Some of it is repeat sequence DNA, which means the same section (the repeating unit) of DNA sequence is present many times, often in close proximity. The length of a repeating unit varies from two to many hundred bases and may be present hundreds of times. Some repeat DNA can be difficult, or impossible, to sequence; a consequence of technical difficulties of working with sections of DNA with unusual chemistry. As a result of this, 8-10% of the human genome will probably remain unsequenced.

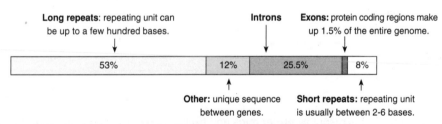

Long repeats: repeating unit can be up to a few hundred bases.

Introns

Exons: protein coding regions make up 1.5% of the entire genome.

| 53% | 12% | 25.5% | 8% |

Other: unique sequence between genes.

Short repeats: repeating unit is usually between 2-6 bases.

Qualities of DNA Sequence Data

The aim of the HGP was to produce a continuous block of sequence information for each chromosome. Initially the sequence information was obtained to draft quality in 2000, with an error rate of 1 in 1000 bases. The **Gold Standard sequence** is high quality with an error rate of <1 per 100 000 bases. This is tenfold better than the original goal and and was obtained following repeated sequencing of the same regions. The Gold Standard was completed in October 2004. Key results of the research are:

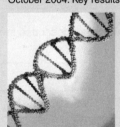

- The analysis suggests that there are perhaps only 20 000-25 000 protein-coding genes in our human genome.
- The number of gaps has been reduced 400-fold to only 341
- It covers 99% of the gene containing parts of the genome and is 99.999% accurate
- The new sequence correctly identifies almost all known genes (99.74%).
- Its accuracy and completeness allows systematic searches for causes of disease.

Genome Research

Benefits and ethical issues arising from the Human Genome Project

Medical benefits

- Improved **diagnosis** of disease and predisposition to disease by genetic testing.
- Better identification of disease carriers, through genetic testing.
- Better **drugs** can be designed using knowledge of protein structure (from gene sequence information) rather than by trial and error.
- Greater possibility of successfully using **gene therapy** to correct genetic disorders.

Non-medical benefits

- Greater knowledge of **family relationships** through genetic testing, e.g. paternity testing in family courts.
- Advances **forensic science** through analysis of DNA at crime scenes.
- Improved knowledge of the evolutionary relationships between humans and other organisms, which will help to develop better, more accurate classification systems.

Possible ethical issues

- It is unclear whether third parties, e.g. health insurers, have rights to genetic test results.
- If treatment is unavailable for a disease, genetic knowledge about it may have no use.
- Genetic tests are costly, and there is no easy answer as to who should pay for them.
- Genetic information is hereditary so knowledge of an individual's own genome has implications for members of their family.

Couples can already have a limited range of genetic tests to determine the risk of having offspring with some disease-causing mutations.

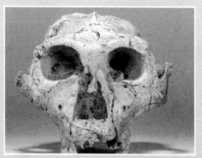

When DNA sequences are available for humans and their ancestors, comparative analysis may provide clues about human evolution.

Legislation is needed to ensure that there is no discrimination on the basis of genetic information, e.g. at work or for health insurance.

1. Briefly describe the objectives of the Human Genome Project (HGP) and the Human Genome Diversity Project (HGDP):

   HGP: _____

   _____

   HGDP: _____

2. Suggest a reason why indigenous peoples around the world are reluctant to provide DNA samples for the HGDP:

   _____

   _____

3. Describe two possible **benefits** of Human Genome Project (HGP):

   (a) Medical: _____

   _____

   (b) Non-medical: _____

   _____

4. Explain what is meant by **proteomics** and explain its significance to the HGP and the ongoing benefits arising from it:

   _____

   _____

   _____

   _____

5. Suggest two possible points of view for one of the **ethical issues** described in the list above:

   (a) _____

   _____

   (b) _____

   _____

Genome Projects

There are many genome projects underway around the world, including the Human Genome Project. The aim of most genome projects is to determine the DNA sequence of the organism's entire genome. Over one hundred bacterial and viral genomes, as well as a number of larger genomes (including honeybee, nematode worm, African clawed frog, pufferfish, zebra fish, rice, cow, dog, and rat) have already been sequenced. Genomes that are, for a variety of reasons, high priority for DNA sequencing include the sea urchin, kangaroo, pig, cat, baboon, silkworm,

rhesus macaque monkey, and turkey. Genome sequencing is very costly, so candidates are carefully chosen. Important factors in this choice include the value of the knowledge to practical applications, the degree of technical difficulty involved, and the size of the genome (currently very large genomes are avoided). Genome sizes and the number of genes per genome vary, and are not necessarily correlated with the size and structural complexity of the organism itself. Once completed, genome sequences are analysed by computer to identify genes.

Artist's impression

Yeast (*Saccharomyces cerevisiae*)

Status: Completed in 1996
Number of genes: 6000
Genome size: 13 Mb

The first eukaryotic genome to be completely sequenced. Yeast is used as a model organism to study human cancer.

Bacteria (*Escherichia coli*)

Status: Completed in 1997
Number of genes: 4403
Genome size: 4.6 Mb

E. coli has been used as a laboratory organism for over 70 years. Various strains of *E. coli* are responsible for several human diseases.

Fruit fly (*Drosophila melanogaster*)

Status: Completed in 2000
Number of genes: 14 000
Genome size: 150 Mb

Drosophila has been used extensively for genetic studies for many years. About 50% of all fly proteins show similarities to mammalian proteins.

Mouse (*Mus musculus*)

Status: Completed in 2002
Number of genes: 30 000
Genome size: 2500 Mb

New drugs destined for human use are often tested on mice because more than 90% of their proteins show similarities to human proteins.

Chimpanzee (*Pan troglodytes*)

Status: Draft, Dec. 2003, Completed, Sept. 2005
Genome size: 3000 Mb

Chimp and human genomes differ by <2%. Identifying differences could provide clues to the genetics of diseases such as cancer, to which chimps are less prone.

Banana (*Musa acuminata*)

Status: In progress. Due 2006
Genome size: 500-600 Mb

The first tropical crop to be sequenced. Bananas have high economic importance. Knowledge of the genome will assist in producing disease resistant varieties of banana.

Maize (*Zea mays*)

Status: In progress
Genome size: 2500 Mb

Maize is a major world crop and an important model organism for studying monocotyledons (including other cereals). The genome contains many repeats, so it will not be fully sequenced.

Chicken (*Gallus gallus*)

Status: Completed in Feb. 2004
Genome size: 1200 Mb

Various human viruses were first found in chickens making this species important for the study of human disease and cross-species transfers. It was the first bird genome to be sequenced.

1. Calculate the number of genes per Mb of DNA for the organisms above:

   (a) Yeast: _____ (b) *E. coli*: _____ (c) Fruit fly: _____ (d) Mouse: _____

2. Suggest why the number of genes per Mb of DNA varies between organisms (hint: consider relative sizes of introns):

   _____

   _____

3. Suggest why researchers want to sequence the genomes of plants such as wheat, rice, and maize:

   _____

   _____

4. Use a web engine search (or read through other parts of this topic) to find:

   (a) **First multicellular animal genome** to be sequenced: _____ Date: _____

   (b) **First plant genome** to be sequenced: _____ Date: _____

Code: RDA 2

Biotechnology Review

This activity is designed to bring together what you have learned over this topic. Complete the table below summarising the major techniques used in the various biotechnological processes and applications. Write in the spaces provided which diagram below (A-G) matches each technique. Keep your responses brief. and as a guide, some have been completed for you.

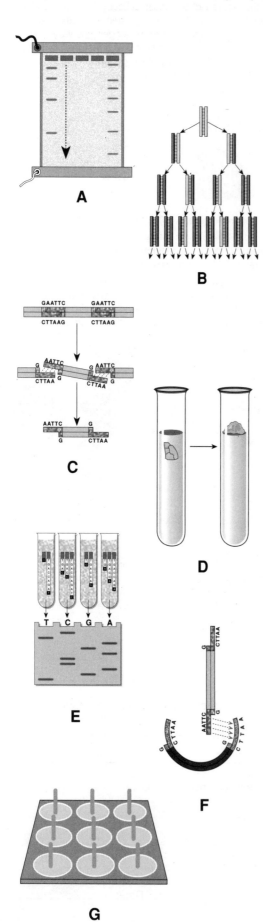

A

B

C

D

E

F

G

Use of Technique		Processes and Applications	
		Gene Cloning	**Transgenesis**
Restriction Enzymes C		The same restriction enzyme (RE) cuts out the gene of interest and opens up the vector, e.g. plasmid DNA or bacteriophage, ready to create the recombinant DNA molecule.	As in gene cloning
Ligation			
Gel Electro-phoresis			
Polymerase Chain Reaction			
DNA Sequencing		not applicable	not applicable
DNA Chips			
Tissue Culture		not applicable	

Processes and Applications			
DNA Profiling	**Genome Analysis**	**Stem Cell Research**	**Xenotransplantation**
Not applicable to profiling using the PCR method. Used in Southern Blotting to cut up the DNA prior to separating the fragments.	REs cut up chromosomes into smaller fragments, which can be manageably sequenced before assembly into a continuous sequence for each chromosome.	not applicable	
not applicable	Used to create a "library" of the DNA fragments by inserting them into separate vectors (e.g. plasmids).	not applicable	
To separate the fragments of DNA by length.	Used (with PCR) to produce a low resolution map of the larger DNA fragments and determine the order of the bases in smaller fragments.	not applicable	
	Used (with gel electrophoresis) to produce a low resolution map of the larger DNA fragments and determine the order of the bases in smaller fragments.	not applicable	
not applicable		not applicable	
		not applicable	
not applicable	not applicable		not applicable

Index